When they sang together it was like making love.

Casey strummed a couple of chords and began in his gravelly voice. "Girl, don't leave me now. Stay with me until the morning light."

Cathleen moved naturally into the next two lines. "And I will show you how to love away the dark and lonely night."

Casey stared into her eyes as he sang, and she gazed back, held captive by him. He sang the suggestive words to her, his eyes conveying everything the lyrics expressed and more. Cathleen responded, the lines coming to her easily, as if there was nothing else she could say.

Then the song was over, and still they could not look away.

KRISTIN JAMES
Morning Star

Silhouette Sensation

*First published in Great Britain in 1993
by Silhouette Books, Eton House, 18-24 Paradise Road,
Richmond, Surrey TW9 1SR*

© Kristin James 1984

Silhouette, Silhouette Sensation and Colophon are
Trade Marks of Harlequin Enterprises B.V.

ISBN 0 373 59048 2

18-9312

Made and printed in Great Britain

Other novels by Kristin James

Silhouette Sensation

Dreams of Evening
The Amber Sky
Worlds Apart
Cutter's Lady
A Very Special Favour
Salt of the Earth
The Letter of the Law

For my father

Chapter 1

CATHLEEN HESITATED OUTSIDE THE FAMILIAR BROWN BRICK building on Music Square West. Her stomach was a writhing mass of nerves. She sat down quickly on the low brick wall bordering the sidewalk and took a deep breath to calm herself. This wasn't the time for an attack of the jitters. The worst thing in the world she could do with a record executive was to go in feeling defeated or desperate. She had to present a picture of utter confidence. Sunburst Records was her last hope. She had to convince them. Otherwise, what would she tell Dusty tomorrow morning?

Cathleen rose, straightened her shoulders and marched up the pebbled concrete walkway to the wide glass doors of Sunburst Records, Inc. She stepped inside and flashed a bright smile at the receptionist who sat behind a polished wood desk.

"I have a five o'clock appointment with Bill McNally." Whoever he was. It galled her that she had been unable to get an interview with the president of the company. After all the things Dusty Richards had done for Sunburst, you'd think John Metcalf would have the courtesy to speak to her. She could remember when she was five years old, and she and Lynette would come to the studio with her parents. John would invite Cathleen and Lynette into his big corner office. He'd give them lollipops and let them bounce on his couch . . . and now he wouldn't even see her.

"Just a moment," the receptionist said with a practiced smile. "I'll tell Mr. McNally you're here."

Cathleen took a seat on the plain blue sofa. They'd redone the waiting room, replacing the old, plush furniture with starkly modern acrylic and glass stuff. Unlike the front of the building, the lobby didn't send a single memory shivering up her spine.

McNally kept her waiting for fifteen minutes before he emerged from his office and strode toward her, extending a small, well-manicured hand. "Miss Richards? How do you do? I'm Bill McNally."

Her nervousness had melted into irritation during the wait, and she replied coolly, "Cathleen Richards."

"Why don't we go back to my office? Would you care for some coffee?"

He was smoother than most of the men she had met in the industry. Cathleen decided that he must be the p.r. man, the one who handled difficult people and got rid of importunate ones like herself. She clenched her fists, digging her fingernails into her palms. Oh, how she wished she didn't have to do this. Any place would have been preferable to Sunburst, where Stella and Casey now reigned supreme. They had broken her father's heart, and now they ruled where Dusty once had. They were Sunburst Records' biggest stars—but they wouldn't have gotten inside the doors if Dusty Richards hadn't opened them.

Cathleen swallowed her anger and smiled sweetly at Bill McNally as she took a seat across from his desk. "Now, what can I do for you?" he began jovially.

"I presume you know who my father is."

"Dusty Richards? Of course. What country and western fan doesn't? He's one of the legends."

"Well, the legend has decided to return to music."

"Oh? How nice."

"Mr. McNally, Dusty's ready to sing again. He wants to cut a new album, and he's already written several songs. Since Sunburst is his old home, naturally he'd like to begin his new career here."

A pained expression crossed the man's face. "Miss Richards, I don't know exactly how to say this. . . . Dusty was once the best. As I said, he's a legend. Let him remain one. Comeback attempts are almost invariably failures. It's been a long time since Dusty was on top. The country and western music industry has changed. He's older. He'd feel out of place. He'd—"

"Dusty Richards would never feel out of place where music is concerned. He still has his talent, and he isn't a relic yet. He's not quite sixty."

The man opposite her combed his fingers through his immaculate iron gray hair and frowned. "I'm trying to be tactful."

"Don't. I'd rather speak openly and honestly."

"All right. The truth is, Dusty Richards is a bad risk. Everyone knows that. He's unreliable. He's always involved in one scandal or another. He gambles and gets into barroom brawls. And he drinks."

"That's Dusty's image. It's part of his appeal. He's the hard-drinking, hard-loving cowboy, not always wise, but very human and easy to identify with."

"It was Dusty's image before he went straight to the bottom of a bottle!" McNally's face was cold, his narrow mouth harsh. "His image since then is more like a skid row bum. You may not remember his last few records, but Sunburst does. He skipped recording sessions time after time. He'd disappear on a three-week drunk when he was supposed to cut an album. He missed performances. Two tours had to be cancelled because he was laid up in the hospital recovering from the d.t.s."

"One of those times he was getting over a car accident."

"Yeah, an accident he had when he was blind drunk and driving eighty miles an hour down a country road. We were lucky the only one he smashed up was himself. I'm sorry to say these things to you, Miss Richards, but you asked for honesty."

"You think I don't know about all that?" Cathleen's wide eyes darkened to a midnight blue, and she leaned forward earnestly. "Believe me, Mr. McNally, I've seen a lot more of Dusty Richards's drunken behavior than this company did. Who do you think cleaned up after him and visited him in the hospital? Or pulled him out of bed in the morning so he'd make a session on time? Or chased him down when the studio called and wanted to know where he was? I know the old Dusty better than any of you. But he's changed."

McNally sighed. "That's what he said every time."

"This is different. Dusty's pulled himself together. He entered Oakcrest Villa nine months ago." Oakcrest was a nearby drug and alcohol rehabilitation clinic famous for its treatment of music stars, sports figures, politicians and actors.

"Good. I'm glad to hear it."

"He's getting out tomorrow. He licked his alcohol problem, and he's eager to return to music. The past is behind him now."

"I'm happy for him."

"But you still won't give him a chance."

"We're not in business to give people chances. Dusty is old news. He wouldn't fit in with modern country and western music."

" 'Blackjack 'n Water' would be as big a hit if it were published today as it was when he recorded it. We both know that. Stella Farrow's still popular."

"Stella's younger than Dusty. He was an established star long before she began. Besides, your mother knows how to change. She's developed, kept pace with the industry."

"She wouldn't even be at this studio if it weren't for Dusty. He brought her here and practically forced you guys to sign her. I heard the story plenty of times when I was a kid. And he gave you C.J. Casey, too. He did more for this company than you could hope to repay." Cathleen's eyes flashed and she rose, fists clenched tightly. "Apparently you've forgotten the money he made for you, all the gold and platinum records."

Bill McNally rose to face her. "No, we haven't forgotten. But neither have we forgotten the money he lost us! Broken contracts, second-rate songs, musicians hired for sessions and studios reserved, only to have Dusty not appear. Maybe he has changed. For his sake I hope so. But I haven't yet met an alcoholic who could stay on the wagon. We can't take the chance he'll be the first."

"God, you're cold!" Color flared in Cathleen's pale cheeks. "When he was on top, everybody loved Dusty. But when his wife left him, broke his heart, and he went down, nobody knew his name. Oh, you're happy to keep his wife. Stella Farrow's a winner. She'd never let emotions interfere with her career. She hasn't enough heart to do that." Rage seared her, but Cathleen bit back the bitter words surging up in her throat. She wasn't about to express her views on her mother to this man. She had vowed long ago not to reveal the pain that Stella's careless, callous desertion of her family had engraved on her own emotions. Cathleen told herself that she felt only contempt for the mother who had had more time for her recording sessions and tours than for her daughters, and who had left her teenage girls and her husband for the sizzling sexual excitement of a younger man.

Cathleen wheeled and stormed out the door, tears of rage blurring her eyes. Why had she come to Sunburst Records? She should have known it would be the same as every other company. No one wanted to take a chance on an alcoholic has-been, no matter how great he had been in his day. But Sunburst's rejection hurt worse because Dusty had been the company's biggest star. It hurt like it had when she had asked Dusty's agent to represent him again, and the agent had laughed in her face.

Head down and half blinded by her tears, she rounded a corner and almost collided with a man coming from the other direction. She swerved, and only the man's hands reaching out to grasp her arms and steady her kept Cathleen from stumbling and falling. "Whoa there, darlin'," a husky male voice cautioned, brimming with laughter.

The sound of his voice went through her like high-voltage electricity. Cathleen knew that voice. Velvet overlaid with sandpaper. A whiskey voice, Lynette called it. Smooth and golden, rich, but with a rough edge. It made one think of bedrooms and tangled sheets, smoke-clouded taverns and mournful honky-tonk songs. She knew the voice, and so did millions of other people who bought his records and rushed to his concerts. It belonged to one of the most popular country and western singers of the day: C.J. Casey.

Cathleen lifted her head, steeling herself to look at him. She'd seen his face on album covers, magazines and newspapers, but not in person for ten years. The tanned skin had acquired more squint lines around the eyes. His coal black hair was brushed with white at the temples. And the beard was new, too. It was a thin, nicely shaped beard which started below his sculpted cheekbones. Two narrow lines of white threaded through the black hair from the ends of his mustache down beside his chin. It gave his face a leaner look, made him seem even sexier, more experienced and dangerous.

The rest of him was the same. Casey had retained his youthful leanness. Long and tall, clad in cowboy boots, jeans and a faded blue work shirt opened three buttons down, his hard body hinted of slow, luxurious loving. And his eyes—still so bright and intense a blue that they pierced her, a startling contrast in the tanned face. His eyelids were heavy, with a sensual droop at the outer corners. His mouth was wide and mobile, and when he smiled the corners of his mouth drew down, showing white, even teeth between his lips. It was a unique smile, appealing and entirely masculine, with no hint of the boyishness most men's smiles revealed. There was no boy to C.J. Casey, never had been. He was raw, lean maleness, every part of him exuding sensuality—from his long, slender callused fingers to his faintly rough face and burning eyes. Casey looked hard and elemental, yet there was sensitivity in his sinewed hands and lines of pain around his eyes and lips that promised gentleness and care in his lovemaking.

Casey stared at her, and Cathleen swallowed. She could feel his gaze all through her body, but she hated to admit that she reacted to him as easily and senselessly as other women did. She despised him. Her father had taken him under his wing when Casey came to Nashville, and had helped set his career on its path. Then Casey had repaid Dusty by having an affair with Dusty's wife. C.J. Casey was the catalyst that had set in motion the events leading to Dusty's drunken downfall.

"I'll be damned!" Casey murmured, his fingers digging into her arms. "Cathleen Richards."

Cathleen's mouth curled, and she jerked away, trying to break his grip on her arms. "Let go of me!"

He grinned. "Same song, second verse. Ten years, and you're still saying the same thing to me."

He was right. She remembered. The last time she had spoken to Casey, she had been crying, her sixteen-year-old soul crushed and disillusioned by what her father had just told her. She had lashed out at Dusty earlier that day, accusing him of driving Stella away with his excessive drinking. His alcoholism had been a lifelong problem, although it hadn't reached its peak until after the divorce. Dusty had retorted that Stella left because she loved another man. She was having an affair with C.J. Casey, Dusty's protégé. Cathleen had fled the room and run outside, dissolving into tears beneath the spreading oak tree in the backyard. After her sobs finally stopped, she had flopped onto her back and stared up at the tangled network of branches. She had recalled the look of love in Casey's eyes when he watched Stella, the way he jumped to do things for her. Oh, yeah, it was there. She should have known it. She would have noticed it if she hadn't been so blinded by her own adolescent crush on Casey. Cathleen hadn't been foolish enough to believe that Casey

would return her teenage love, but his dishonesty and
betrayal of her father had destroyed her tender, idealized
vision of him. Her love had turned to hate in that moment,
and the change had torn her heart.

Then Casey had come around the side of the house,
calling her name. When he saw her on the ground, he had
run and knelt beside her, pulling her up, his hands digging
into her flesh as they did now. "What the hell is going on?"
he had asked roughly. "Dusty won't see me, and you're
lying out here crying. What's the matter?"

"I hate you," she had replied, her voice apathetic in the
aftermath of emotional loss. "Dusty and Lynette and I
don't ever want to see you again." He had made an
exasperated sound deep in his throat, his face thunderous,
and she knew he had wanted to shake her, but he hadn't.
"Let go of me," she had ordered, and he had.

This time he didn't. Instead, his grin broadened, and he
joked, "Tears become you more now. Boy, I gotta say, you
grew up nicely." His eyes admired her, sliding from her
face to her full breasts and narrow waist.

Cathleen grimaced. She disliked her old-fashioned figure. It was a Gibson Girl shape, with an absurdly small
waist, full bosom, and wide, softly curving hips. It drew
leering looks and wolf whistles from men on the street,
and far too many "accidental" touches at parties. She had
developed her lush figure early, and the attention she had
received from older men had confused and distressed her,
making her embarrassed about her body. Boys her age had
been frightened by her too-soon-mature shape and left her
alone. Later Cathleen had learned to turn aside smutty
remarks with a witty retort and to avoid the groping
hands. She had even found a man or two willing to talk
and laugh with her instead of immediately pulling her into
his bed. But she remained self-conscious about her body
and usually wore suits or dresses with concealing jackets.

"Would you please let go of me?" she requested,
striving for an icy tone.

"Not till you agree to have a cup of coffee with me and

explain why you're crying in the middle of Sunburst Records."

"I don't want to have a cup of coffee with you—or anything else."

"Still carrying that giant chip on your shoulder? Well, at least answer one question. Is it true Dusty's gone dry? Somebody told me he's in the Villa and getting better."

"Yes, it's true." She glared straight into his eyes, proud to let him know that Dusty had finally recovered from the blow Casey and Stella had dealt him.

"Good. I'm glad to hear it. So your tears don't have anything to do with him?"

"No! They have to do with this rotten company and all the others like it who won't give Dusty another chance."

"He wants to sing again?" Casey released her and she stepped back a little, but didn't move away from him.

"Yes. He's talked about it for weeks now. He's sure he can do it. He wrote some songs, and he wants to record a couple of mine."

"You write songs?"

"Not for a living. Not yet, anyway."

"You sing, too?"

She shook her head. "No. I mean, yes, I sing. We all sing. But I'm not a professional singer. I'm more a background person."

"I remember." He took one arm and turned her around, guiding her along the hall. "How about that cup of coffee? Maybe I could help, you know."

"I don't want your help," she retorted automatically.

"Cathy, darlin', you're not a kid anymore. Can't you let go of this crazy grudge?"

"No. And don't make it sound like a foolish nothing."

He cast her a speaking glance, but made no comment. Not knowing exactly why she consented, Cathleen let him lead her to the small lounge area of the building, a little white-walled room filled with candy and drink machines and small plastic tables and chairs. She glanced around in surprise. "What's this? What happened to the coffee shop? The one with the little counter and the stools that turned around?"

"Not profitable enough. They closed it and ripped out the counter and stools to put in a microwave and machines. You can get anything here, though. Coffee? A sweet roll?"

"Casey, this isn't breakfast. It's almost six in the evening."

He shrugged. "I just got up a couple of hours ago. Okay, how about a cola? A candy bar?" He walked over to peer into one of the machines. "This one has sandwiches, I think. A little green around the edges maybe . . ."

"Thanks. You make it sound very appetizing. I'll have a Dr. Pepper."

He plunked several coins into a machine and two cans of soda rolled out. Casey set them down on the minuscule table where Cathleen sat and straddled a chair across from her. "What do you do with yourself besides write songs?"

"I work for Eddy Lambert," she said, naming a successful agent in Nashville. "I'm his secretary."

"So you're a secretary who secretly writes songs and must have a good voice if genes mean anything, yet isn't a professional singer. Don't you want to be a singing star and make a million dollars?" he joked.

"Oh, I wouldn't mind making a million dollars," she countered, smiling.

Casey's hand paused in the act of raising the drink to his lips, and he stared at her, strangely stunned somewhere in his solar plexis. He'd forgotten Cathleen's smile. It could lift clouds and make a man's stomach do flip-flops. She wasn't as pretty as her sister Lynette, because she resembled Dusty too much. Her hair was thick and brown, the color of dark chocolate, not the light sun-kissed chestnut of Stella and Lynette. Her face was a feminine version of Dusty's, the nose too pug, the mouth too wide, the shape too square for real beauty. Only her expressive dark blue eyes outlined by smoky lashes made her face arresting— and that heartbreaking smile. Casey remembered Dusty joking about it one day, saying she'd had it even as a child. One of her many sitters had once admitted that she couldn't punish Cathleen because she would smile up at her so sweetly that the woman couldn't believe Cathleen had done anything wrong.

Well, she still had the smile, only now it turned a man's knees to water, Casey thought. His eyes dropped to the thrust of her breasts against her dress, enjoying the ultrawomanly curves of her figure. With the kind of body she had, he doubted whether most men got around to looking at her face. He wondered what she looked like without clothes. Cathleen glanced at him and blushed, looking away. It was clear from his heavy-lidded gaze exactly where his mind was. She flushed uncomfortably, and to get his mind off her body, she jumped into the subject she hadn't meant to discuss. "I've been trying to get someone to record Dusty, but no one will. There's no loyalty in this town."

"That's not true. There are a lot of singers who feel loyalty and good will for Dusty. Everybody's happy about his recovery."

"Maybe. But that doesn't apply to the agents and record companies. Nobody wants to take a chance on him. Including Sunburst Records and his old agent. Joe Siegel practically kicked me out of his office."

"Siegel's a—" He stopped and obviously changed his wording. "An idiot. Once you wrong Joe, you're dead with him. After Dusty cancelled those two tours Joe arranged, he'd never take him on again."

"Well, neither will anybody else."

"Dusty made himself quite a reputation the past few years. He's known to be 'difficult to work with.'"

"He was. I'm aware of what a pain he can be. But he's kicked the alcohol. He's clean. I mean, he's straight as an arrow. He needs something to do. How long do you think he'll last on the wagon if he has nothing to occupy his time and mind? He has to work, or sheer boredom will send him back to the bars and his old running buddies. Why can't someone give him a chance to prove he's changed?"

"Tell you what. Let me see what I can do. I'll drop in on John Metcalf and see if he won't listen to Dusty. How would that be?"

Cathleen opened her mouth to refuse any help from him, then stopped. It galled her to accept a favor from Casey, but how could she refuse when it would help Dusty? She must not allow her own pride to stand in the way of Dusty's recovery. "I guess you owe him," she murmured.

"Yeah," Casey agreed softly. "I owe him." He rose and pointed an admonitory finger at her. "You sit right here. I'll be back in a minute."

Cathleen obeyed him, her mind churning with doubts. Should she have let him help? Would it disturb Dusty? It had been years since he'd expressed any anger at Casey, but this might stir it up. But working would be the best thing for Dusty. She was still vacillating almost twenty minutes later when Casey returned to the coffee room. With a spurt of resentment she noted that he had obviously had no trouble getting in to see the president of Sunburst, even without an appointment.

"Well, darlin', it's all set," Casey told her, grinning the familiar upside-down smile. "I figured it'd be better if John saw Dusty and listened to his songs informally. No need for Dusty to come to the studio for an audition."

"Thank you." She was amazed at his sensitivity.

He shrugged. "Is tomorrow night too soon?"

"No. That'd be perfect." She knew Dusty would be buoyed by the idea that the president of Sunburst was after him to record the day he got out. The familiar world of the music industry would help ease the raw strangeness of being outside the clinic after so long.

"Good. Hope you don't mind. I invited us to dinner."

She stared. "What? You're coming, too? No."

Casey chuckled. "Your hospitality overwhelms me."

"It's impossible. Surely you must see that. Dusty isn't up to facing you the day he leaves the Villa."

"Because he got mad at me ten years ago? Hell, honey, Dusty Richards has had more drunken fights with more people than I can count. If he avoided us all, he wouldn't speak to half of Nashville. He'll be okay."

Cathleen gritted her teeth. Casey might be right. Dusty was hot-tempered and quick to take offense, but just as quick to forgive and forget. He could be easygoing to a degree Cathleen couldn't fathom, smiling and joking with a man he'd earlier accused of stabbing him in the back. When she questioned Dusty about such contradictory behavior he would grin and drawl, "Ah, he ain't so bad, just makes mistakes once in a while." It was occasionally infuriating, but it was also one of the qualities that made it hard to dislike Dusty, no matter how obnoxious he was at times.

But though her father might be able to handle Casey's presence, Cathleen wasn't so sure she could. She found it harder to forgive than Dusty did. She didn't like Casey and hated feeling obligated to him. She would hate even more being pleasant to him for a whole evening. Most of all, Casey's blatant sexual appeal disturbed her. It had shocked her to realize that she responded to his slow, sexy grin and his aura of sensuality. It wouldn't do to go dry in the mouth, her heart accelerating, at the sight of a man she despised.

Seeing her hesitation, Casey pressed, "Come on, you can't refuse to give me a meal after I've wangled you a home visit from John Metcalf."

Cathleen glared. He was right again. She couldn't be so rude and thankless as to refuse him dinner when he'd done her a favor. "Oh, all right," she agreed gracelessly. "Is seven too early? We don't have a cocktail hour anymore."

"Fine," he agreed pleasantly, as if she hadn't been insultingly reluctant to have his company. "I'll bring John. That way I can be sure he won't back out. Now, where do you live?"

She told him and was glad he didn't register any surprise at the unfashionable address. Few people realized how Dusty had wasted his fortune. Although he continued to receive some royalties on songs he had written, Cathleen had had to get a job to help support them. If Jack

Beaudry, her father's most loyal friend, hadn't paid the
bill at Oakcrest, she would have had to sell their house to
keep Dusty in the expensive rehabilitation clinic.

Casey wrote her address and brief directions to it on a
scrap of paper and tucked it into the tight hip pocket of his
nondesigner jeans. "Can I give you a ride home?" he
asked.

"No, thanks. I have my car."

"Okay." He hesitated another moment. "Well, see you
tomorrow night."

"Yeah."

He swung away and disappeared down the hall. Cathleen remained standing where she was, still stunned by the
way things had turned out. She had swung from the
near-despair of McNally's refusal to the unexpected high
of John Metcalf's agreeing to hear Dusty's new songs. She
resented the fact that C.J. Casey had been the one to bring
about the chance, and she was filled with a funny half-
excitement, half-fear to think that Casey would be coming
with Metcalf to her house. She didn't want him there. And
there was something stronger than dislike behind that
feeling.

Chapter 2

CATHLEEN WALKED OUT THE FRONT DOORS AND DOWN THE shallow steps to the parking lot. Her car, a battered VW bug kept alive long past its prime by Jack Beaudry's constant attention, was parked on the far side of the lot in the shade of a large tree. As Cathleen ambled toward it, she drew in a deep breath. The air smelled like spring, an elusive fragrance that was a unique combination of warmth, fresh rain and newly dug earth. It was the first time she'd noticed it—or the faint green frosting on the tree branches which indicated that leaves soon would burst forth.

The fragile white dogwood and bright redbud were probably blooming now along the winding drive to Greenwood. She smiled faintly at the memory of their beauty, but there was an ache in her chest, too. It had been ten years since she'd been at Greenwood. Stella had kept the house after the divorce—and given the kids to Dusty.

Cathleen suddenly wanted to see her sister. She glanced at her watch and decided that it wasn't so late that she would interrupt Lynette's dinner. She could tell Lynette the exciting news and invite her to go tomorrow to pick up their father. There wasn't much likelihood Lynette would come. Much as Cathleen loved her sister, she knew that Lynette avoided anything painful or emotional. It was part of her legacy from their parents' battle-scarred marriage.

It wasn't a long trip to Lynette's red-brick home in Belle Meade, Nashville's "old money" community, and soon Cathleen pulled into the narrow side driveway and stopped at the rear of the mansion. A maid answered her knock on the kitchen door and greeted her with a smile, informing her that Lynette was in the small den. The loud clack of Cathleen's heels on the wooden hallway flooring gave away her presence, and Lynette stuck her head out the farthest door. "Cathleen!" she exclaimed with genuine pleasure. "What are you doing here? I didn't know you were coming by today."

"I hadn't planned to, but I wanted to tell you my news."

Lynette's expressive hazel eyes widened in hopeful expectation. "You're getting married!"

Cathleen laughed. "Hardly. Don't you think about anything else?"

Lynette tilted her head prettily, her mouth drawing up into a thoughtful pout. "Almost never," she admitted after a moment of mock-grave thought. "Come in and let me fix you a drink. I was having a whiskey sour while I waited for Michael."

"I'll have a vodka Collins." Cathleen rarely drank. Although she didn't shun alcohol with fear and loathing as did some relatives of alcoholics, there were too many bad memories associated with it for her to really enjoy it. It seemed as though she'd spent half her life searching out her father's hiding places and dumping the contents of the bottles down the sink. As Lynette mixed her a healthy drink, Cathleen again experienced a little nip of fear that Lynette might follow in their father's footsteps. It was another worry the child of an alcoholic lived with—the anxiety that heredity would betray her into drunkenness. In fact, Lynette didn't drink any more than most people.

Cathleen settled into the least uncomfortable chair in

the room—Lynette's furniture was bought more to be looked at than sat in—and sipped at the cool drink. Lynette plopped down on the coffee table across from her, managing to look graceful even in the peculiar location. It struck Cathleen anew how beautiful her sister was. Designer clothes and constant attention to hair and face helped, but Lynette was also graced with natural loveliness. Her figure was tall and slender, perfect for clothes, and her hair was a rich chestnut highlighted by streaks of gold. She and Cathleen both possessed white skin tinted with natural color, but Lynette had turned hers a pale gold by assiduous tanning. The features of her delicate triangular face were perfectly balanced, and her large eyes were an intriguing green brown, with a wide gold ring around the pupil. She resembled their mother, who was known for her looks, but Lynette surpassed her.

"So?" Lynette prodded. "What's going on?"

Cathleen smiled. "John Metcalf agreed to listen to Dusty's new songs. I think he'll sign him if he likes them."

"Are they any good?" Lynette asked doubtfully.

"Yes. He's back to his old form. They aren't like the trash he was writing a few years ago."

"How did you get Metcalf to agree? Don't tell me he did it out of love for Dad. The last time they were together Dusty took a swing at him."

"Did he? Oh, that's right." Cathleen giggled. "I'd forgotten. No wonder he wouldn't see me. I was palmed off onto the vice-president in charge of getting rid of pests."

"But I thought you said—"

"I wasn't the one who persuaded Metcalf to listen to Dusty. C.J. Casey did."

"Casey?" Lynette echoed in amazement. "But why? Dusty worse than took a swing at him. Remember?"

"Yeah, I remember." Cathleen doubted that she'd ever forget the wild scene which had taken place a few days after she'd cried and screamed at Casey to get out of their lives. Dusty and the two girls had moved into their new home, leaving Stella with the mansion named after her biggest hit single. Casey had dropped by to talk to Dusty. Dusty, wild and drunk, had flung open the front door and pitched into him, knocking him clean off the front porch with his first blow. Casey rose to his feet, shaking his head to clear it. Bits of moist black earth clung to his clothes, and blood trickled from his mouth, splashing onto his shirt and the white concrete walkway. For an instant, rage had flared in his bright blue eyes and Casey's fists had clenched. Standing at the living room window, Cathleen had seen what took place. She ran to the porch to stop Casey, knowing that her drunken father was no match for the younger, stronger man.

But before she could reach them Dusty had lurched down the porch and swung again. Casey didn't hit him, just stepped back to avoid the blow. Again Dusty swung and missed. The impetus of his movement carried him around and forward, and he toppled over ignominiously in the mud. Casey stood for a moment looking down at Dusty scrambling in the soft earth. He made a low, disgusted sound. "Damn it, Dusty, this is the last time. You aren't worth the effort." His hard blue gaze flicked up to Cathleen on the porch. "Take him inside and put him to bed. I'm sure he can't manage it on his own." That had been the last time she saw Casey face to face until this afternoon.

"I remember," Cathleen repeated softly, then shrugged, returning to the present. "Who knows why Casey wanted to help? Guilt, I suppose. I ran into him—literally—after I left Bill McNally's office. He insisted I sit down and have a soft drink with him. He asked about Dusty, and when I told him the trouble I'd had finding anyone who'd take a chance on Dad, he offered to help. He owes Dad something, so I agreed. He talked to John Metcalf, and John said he'd listen to Dusty tomorrow evening."

"The first day? Won't it be too much for Dusty?"

"He's eager to return. He'll be scared, but not any worse than if he sits around for days worrying about it.

Besides, it'll make him feel good to think Sunburst wants him."

"I hope so. When's he coming home?"

"Ten tomorrow morning. Want to come with me?"

Lynette wrinkled her nose. "No! I'll leave it to you. I hate institutions. Dusty'll understand."

"I'm sure he will." Dusty hated to face unpleasant things even more than Lynette did. "Why don't you have lunch with us?"

"Okay. I'll take us out. That'd be fun."

"Sure. Whatever you want." Lynette asked about Cathleen's job, and Cathleen shrugged, replying, "You know how it is. It keeps me busy. At least it's interesting. Today I typed the road schedule for the Backstreet Band's next tour. It's better than typing legal contracts."

"I don't understand why you do it."

"Because it pays fairly well, it's entertaining and there aren't many jobs around for music majors."

"If you'd take the allowance Mother gives you . . ."

"Let's not get into that again. You know I don't want her money. She's trying to salve her conscience, and I have no intention of making it easy for her. It would make me feel disloyal."

"Meaning I'm disloyal because *I* take it?"

"No. It's different for you. You love her. You have a more normal mother/daughter relationship, but Stella and I parted ways long ago. I can't be a hypocrite and accept money from her when I don't like her."

"You accepted a favor from Casey," Lynette pointed out.

"That's different. It was for Dusty. Besides, C.J. Casey *ought* to do him a favor."

Lynette studied her drink. "Do you think Casey had an affair with Mother?"

Cathleen stared. "Of course. Don't you?"

Lynette shrugged. "Dusty's been known to make things up before. Why wouldn't it have come out in the divorce proceedings?"

"Because Dusty loved Stella too much to put her through it."

"A lot of other skeletons fell out of the closet. He wasn't quiet about her other affairs."

"What about the reports in the newspapers?"

"Rumors. You know how reporters are. Dusty's punching Casey in the nose made it look suspicious. But I never saw him at Greenwood when I'd visit Mother."

"Don't you remember how Casey looked at Stella? When Dusty told me, I knew it had to be true, because Casey looked at her with his heart in his eyes."

"Um-hum. Like you looked at him."

"Lynette!"

"Well, it's true, isn't it? Didn't you have a gigantic crush on Casey?"

"Maybe. What does that have to do with anything?"

Lynette shrugged. "Maybe nothing. But perhaps it added to your hurt and resentment of Casey."

"Lyn, what is this about? Surely you aren't concerned about whether Stella and Casey had an affair ten years ago!"

"No. I'm beating around the bush. Sometimes . . . sometimes I'm afraid you'd hate me if I did something wrong."

"Don't be silly." Cathleen leaned forward and touched her sister's arm. "Lynette, I'll always love you. Dusty hasn't exactly been an angel, and I love him. What's the matter?"

Lynette hesitated. "I'm just not a good person like you are."

Cathleen laughed. "I'm not good. We were just discussing the way I hold grudges. I've never forgiven Stella for leaving Dusty."

"And us."

"And us."

"She's not a bad person, just selfish. So am I."

"Lyn, would you please tell me what you're talking about?"

Lynette shrugged. "Things don't seem to be going well at the moment."

"Are you and Michael having problems?"

"Of course not. People like the Stokes don't have marital problems. Didn't you know that? They just smile and hate each other's guts." She swung away. Cathleen rose and started toward her, but she heard the kitchen door close and a heavy tread in the hallway. Lynette fixed a pleasant expression on her face as she turned toward the door. "Michael, is that you?"

"Yeah." He paused in the door frame. "Hi, honey, fix me a Scotch and water, would you? Why, Cathleen, what a nice surprise. I didn't know you were coming tonight."

"I wasn't. It was a spur of the moment thing."

"You'll stay for supper, won't you?" He set down his briefcase and advanced into the room to give her a quick hug. Michael was a tall, good-looking, affable man who was very much in love with Lynette. Cathleen wondered what had happened between him and her sister. There was no possibility of talking to Lynette about it now that Michael was home. She'd have to catch Lynette later, after Dusty got out of the clinic. She'd invite Lynette to the house for a nice long chat one Saturday afternoon.

Cathleen turned down Michael's invitation. "I better not. I just dropped by to tell Lynette something."

Several minutes of good-byes and hospitable invitations passed before Cathleen was able to leave. Driving home, she pondered Lynette's unexplained comments. Was there really a rift between her and Michael, or was she exaggerating, as Lynette was prone to do? Perhaps an ordinary argument had appeared more serious to Lynette than it really was. Cathleen hoped that was the case. Dusty's homecoming would be enough for her to deal with, without Lynette's marriage falling apart, too.

When she reached the small frame house where she and Dusty had lived for the past two years Cathleen felt unutterably tired. Her footsteps lagged as she crossed the narrow concrete driveway and went up the three stone steps to the side door. The door opened into the kitchen; Cathleen stepped inside and tossed her purse onto the table. It occurred to her that her sudden slump was probably the result of not eating until far later than normal. As usual, she was on a diet to curb her lush figure, and it had been a long time since the meager hard-boiled egg and salad she'd consumed for lunch. Cathleen cut up ingredients for a large salad and peeled an orange, took one look at the pitiful excuse for a meal and dived back into the refrigerator to make a sandwich.

She had just finished the deliciously thick ham sandwich and was far more cheerful when the telephone rang. Cathleen padded across the kitchen to answer it. "Hello?"

"Hey, little one, you sound chipper."

"Hi, Jack." She smiled, recognizing the soft Alabama drawl of Jack Beaudry, her father's best friend. Although he had never attained the superstar status of Dusty and Casey, Jack had been a steady, popular singer since his youth, first in a family group and then on his own. Strangely enough, he had become more popular as his career lengthened. For the past few years his easygoing style and low, whispery voice had attracted the newer fans of country and western music. More important to Cathleen, he was one of the few friends who had stood by Dusty through thick and thin, enduring his excesses and insults and patiently doing him favor after favor.

"I guess you're happy about Dusty's coming home," Jack went on lazily.

"Of course."

"When are you driving up there?"

"I'm picking him up at ten."

"Want some company?"

"Oh, Jack, would you?" Cathleen cried delightedly. "I'd love for you to come with me. Frankly, I'm rather nervous, and Lynette didn't want to go."

"No. Lynette's not big on facing things."

"She cares for Dusty." Cathleen automatically defended her sister.

"Hold on, don't get prickly. I know Lynette, too. She's

a sweet kid. I remember her sitting out in the back swing talking to me after Sally died. Nobody helped me like she did. But she hates to face hard things."

Cathleen smiled, picturing his lackadaisical shrug. "Okay, Jack. Sorry. If you're willing to go to the Villa, I'd love your company."

"I'll pick you up tomorrow a little before nine."

"Thank you. I appreciate it."

"Come on, honey, you'll embarrass me. See you tomorrow."

They exchanged good-byes and hung up. Cathleen's spirits lightened even more. She had been nervous about going alone. Dusty seemed much better than ever before. He was willing to admit past mistakes with brutal honesty. His frenetic gaiety, which could change instantly into towering rage, had been replaced by a hard-won calm. She doubted that Dusty could be anything but optimistic, but he had abandoned lies and rosy picture painting. He realized what he'd done to his career and appeared ready to face a hard trip back.

However, you never knew with Dusty. Cathleen loved her father and defended him staunchly against outsiders, but she had taken care of him too long not to fear a return to his drunken binges. She could never be completely free of the bad feelings of the past: the long nights of worry; the fear that he would kill himself or somebody else in a drunken accident; the bitter disappointment of his broken promises; the irrepressible resentment at cleaning up after him or putting him to bed yet another time. The dread of it happening again lingered at the back of her mind.

Mingled with her happiness and fear was a sadness that she would no longer be alone in the house. It had been pleasant the past few months, not having to look after anyone else or put up with company she didn't want. Fighting that emotion was a hope she didn't express aloud for fear of its being dashed: If Dusty were all right, after a settling-in period he wouldn't need her to look after him anymore. She could get her own apartment. She could be free of the heavy burden she had carried for years.

With such complex, conflicting emotions, Cathleen wasn't surprised that she had difficulty getting to sleep, or that she slept lightly and dreamed often. It was almost a relief when her alarm broke her sleep.

She showered, dressed and was ready long before Jack arrived. He was on time, an unusual event for him, and Cathleen knew it was a measure of his concern for her and Dusty. A warm smile hovered about her lips as she watched Jack stroll up the sidewalk to the front door. He was the opposite of Dusty in personality and appearance. Dusty was short, dark and intense, his wiry frame and dark blue eyes radiating energy. He was changeable and charming. Jack, on the other hand, was slow, steady and comfortable to be around. His hair was a wavy rust brown touched with gray at the temples, his eyes a common brown. The rough-featured, craggy face was barely short of homely, but the warmth of his personality imbued it with a certain appeal. Jack reminded Cathleen of an ugly hound you couldn't resist taking home. Tall and lanky, he walked with an unhurried, slouching gait. His speech was equally slow. He sang and spoke in a husky half-whisper that sounded as if he'd sung too many songs and smoked too many cigarettes.

Cathleen had known Jack since she was a child. Although he was nearly fifteen years younger than her father, he had been in country and western music almost as long. He started singing with his family as a child and became friends with Dusty about the same time he split with his family's gospel group, two facts that Cathleen suspected were closely related. He visited their house often, and though Lynette, older than Cathleen by two years, claimed she could remember a time before Jack Beaudry, Cathleen could not. In a business known for its crushing effect on marriages, he had managed the feat of staying married to his teenage sweetheart for twenty years. Sally, his wife, had died four years ago, and he had not remarried.

Jack was just as faithful to his friends. He stuck by

Dusty, visiting him, helping Cathleen find him when he went on week-long binges, often driving Dusty home and putting him to bed. He had thrown several jobs Dusty's way after his career had failed, and had recorded a couple of Dusty's old songs in order to give him royalty money. When Cathleen needed a job, he had persuaded his agent, Eddy Lambert, to make the inexperienced girl his secretary. Oakcrest Villa refused to reveal the name of the anonymous benefactor who had paid for Dusty's treatment, but it hadn't taken much figuring for Cathleen to know it was Jack.

Cathleen opened the door before he got to it, a welcoming smile on her face. "Hi! Thanks for bringing the Lincoln."

"I figured it would be better than the pickup. Dusty'll want to leave the Villa in style."

Cathleen stood on tiptoe to peck him on the cheek. "Want some coffee before we go?"

"That's tempting. You know I love your coffee, but we'll be late if we don't hit the road."

He escorted her to her side of the car, then got into the driver's seat and whipped out of the driveway. Cathleen tensed for a fast ride. Jack's driving was the one way in which he was similar to Dusty. They both drove like maniacs. He took I65 south and split off on Murfreesboro Pike. Long before they reached Murfreesboro, he turned onto a narrow, winding country road leading to Oakcrest Villa.

They made casual conversation for a time. Jack asked about Lynette and about Cathleen's job. She replied lightly, and in turn inquired about his most recent tour. "I'm getting too old for the road," he replied with a laugh. "Maybe I ought to settle down."

"Hah! You're like Dusty. Inside a month you'd be bored stiff and asking Eddy why he hadn't booked you for anything."

"You may be right," he agreed good-naturedly.

They fell silent. Cathleen watched the gently rolling

countryside beyond the highway, enjoying the trees fuzzed with pale green and the colorful mixture of lavender wisteria, pink-purple redbud, and white dogwood and bridal wreath. Here and there cheerful yellow jonquils bobbed their heavy heads in front of a roadside home. A bubbling happiness seized Cathleen's heart, and a song formed in her head, a lyrical tune as sprightly and bouncing as her mood. She began to hum, keeping time with her fingers on her denim-clad knees.

"That's pretty," Jack commented, and she stopped, startled.

"Oh. I didn't realize—was I doing it out loud?"

"Yeah, it sounded nice. What was it?"

She shrugged. "Something that popped into my head."

"Why won't you let me look at your songs? I could probably use some. I can't write songs myself."

"Because I'm afraid you'd buy them out of the kindness of your heart, not because they were good. I want someone to sing them because they like them, because they're too good to turn down."

"It doesn't hurt to rely on your friends in this business. It takes more than quality to get a song recorded."

"I know."

"But you still won't let me help?"

"No."

"You are one stubborn lady. You must be related to Dusty."

"I can't explain it well, but recording a song as a favor is different from the things you've done for Dusty and me in the past. Don't get me wrong. I'm very appreciative. But landing me a job or paying for Dusty's treatment doesn't give me any illusions about my talent or salability, which—"

"Whoa, hold on there, girl. What do you mean, paying for Dusty's treatment?"

"At the Villa. Don't try that innocent look on me. It had to be you. Who else would pay for Dusty?"

"I'd like to lay claim to your gratitude, but, honey, it

wasn't me. I swear it. I called the place to let 'em know I'd be good for the bill, and they told me it had been taken care of. I figured Lynette's husband did it, or you scraped up the money somehow."

Cathleen stared. "Are you telling me the truth?"

"Honest. I didn't pay for it."

"Then who did?" she exclaimed, and Jack shrugged. "It couldn't have been Michael, or Lynette would have told me. Besides, he doesn't have much faith in treatment centers like that. I sure didn't have the money for it."

"It was probably someone who figured they owed Dusty a favor. He has more friends than you think. Dusty helped a lot of us through some hard times. Most people couldn't take being around him, and they got tired of giving him business because he'd screw it up. But paying for his treatment's different. Hell, I can think of fifty people who might have done it."

"Can you? I could only think of one—you." She bit her lip thoughtfully. "I wonder who it was."

"No point worrying about it. They don't want thanks or they'd have let you know their name."

"It makes me feel strange, not knowing."

"Just accept it. I believe that when you need help, it always turns up. Something Dusty did a long time ago came back to him when he needed it."

"Why, Jack, I believe you never lost your gospel-group mentality," Cathleen teased.

He grinned lazily. "Don't you believe it. I'm a wild man."

"Uh-huh."

They passed between the massive brick gateposts marking the entrance to the Villa grounds. The collection of modern buildings in the distance seemed out of place in the quiet, cedar-studded environment. Jack pulled to a stop under the wide porte cochere of the main building. Taking a deep breath, Cathleen stepped out of the car and marched into the lobby.

Anticlimactically, there was no sign of Dusty. They had to wait almost twenty minutes for him to finish his departure session with his therapist. Finally Cathleen caught sight of Dusty's spare, energetic figure striding down the main hall toward them, and she rose, her heart suddenly choking her throat. Tears sparkled in her eyes. He looked so good, so much like he had in earlier years. He was dressed in one of his old outfits, black denim slacks and a black satin shirt with silver piping. The expensive ostrich-skin boots which he had kept through even his worst financial times gleamed on his feet, and he carried a black felt cowboy hat with silver and black braid trim on the crown. He had lost the puffiness of drinking in his months in the Villa, and many hours spent walking the grounds and exercising in the weight room had turned him tanned and lean. Except for the lack of jewelry he could have been himself fifteen years ago—but even then his eyes hadn't been as clear or his expression as calm.

"Hello, Dad," Cathleen said simply, stepping into his arms and hugging him.

"Hi, honey. Look who's here. Hey, Jack, how ya doing?"

"Great. How about you?"

"Couldn't be better. You're looking at a free man." His blue eyes twinkled, the leathery creases around his eyes crinkling. Dusty Richards was a good-looking man, his face saved from handsomeness by an almost boyishly pug nose and deep lines of experience. He was a charmer, an exuberant personality who drew people effortlessly, and, like his daughter, he possessed a smile that melted hearts. Neither Cathleen nor Jack was immune to it, and they grinned back at him now, suddenly brimming with a formless hope.

It didn't take long to stow Dusty's possessions in the trunk. Then they hopped into the car, Cathleen settling into the plush back seat with a smile. She watched her father as Jack roared down the gravel drive toward the gates. His fists were clenched on his knees, and his eyes took in the surrounding landscape, though he hardly moved his head. When they passed through the gates he let out a sharp whoop and turned to her. "Baby, it's all behind me now. I'm starting a brand new life!"

Chapter 3

On the ride home they fell into an awkward silence. Cathleen hated to jump in first thing with her news about John Metcalf, but she could think of little else. She prompted Jack to talk about his latest tour. Dusty listened politely, but his mind was obviously not on the subject. He glanced around and wiped his palms on his knees. When they reached the outskirts of Nashville he leaned forward to take in the familiar landmarks.

"Boy, it's good to be home," he exclaimed. "I never thought this town could look so pretty—or so scary."

"Nervous?" Jack asked.

"I feel like a fifteen-year-old kid following a hooker into her room." He swung around to speak to Cathleen. "What'd you find out, honey? Anybody willing to take a chance on this old man?"

"How would you feel about returning to Sunburst?" Cathleen asked with the studied casualness of someone dropping a bombshell.

Dusty gaped. "You're joking! Last time I saw John

Metcalf he told me I was through with Sunburst and everybody else in music."

"He must have changed his mind."

Dusty snorted. "More likely someone did a little arm twisting. I wonder who. Stella?"

"It was C.J. Casey. I met him in the hall at Sunburst, and he spoke to Mr. Metcalf." Cathleen paused, waiting for Dusty's explosion.

"Casey?" was all he said. "Lord, I haven't seen him in years. Well, that's good of him."

Cathleen breathed a little easier at his mild reaction. "Metcalf's coming to the house tonight to listen to you, and Casey'll be with him." She might as well get it all over with at once.

"Tonight?" His eyebrows shot up, and for an instant his face was filled with panic. "I can't—" He pulled his features under control. "I guess it's better than sitting around thinking about it. And Casey will be there. It'll practically be a jam session." He relaxed, turning back to gaze out the front window. He began to plan, his voice growing lighter and more eager with each word. "We can do that song of yours, 'Dreamer.' We sound good together on that. I'll do 'Jewel.' How many do you suppose he wants to hear? Maybe you could sing one of your songs."

"Wait a minute," Cathleen began. "I'm not the one who wants to cut an album."

"It'll make it easier, more informal."

"Dusty, I don't want to sing."

Jack twisted in his seat and shot her a meaningful glance. "Come on, Cathleen, what's wrong with singing a song or two?"

Cathleen shut her mouth. Jack was right. What was wrong with her singing tonight if it would put Dusty at ease? She knew she had reacted negatively to Dusty's idea because the thought of singing in front of Casey filled her with uneasiness. This was no time to be frightened off. Dusty needed all her support. "Okay, okay," she agreed in mock disgust. "It's unfair, the two of you ganging up on me."

Dusty replied as lightly as she had, and they spent the
rest of the trip making plans for the evening. When they
reached the house Jack departed almost immediately.
Lynette dropped in a few minutes later and swept them
out to lunch at an elegant restaurant. After lunch Cathleen
left Dusty and Lynette at home while she bought groceries
for the evening meal. She was a good cook and planned to
make her best dinner. After she shopped, she gave the
house a quick cleaning, mentally thanking her boss again
for giving her the day off to get Dusty settled. Dusty
insisted on rearranging the furniture two or three times to
achieve the best arrangement for informality and acoustics. Finally she was able to escape to their small kitchen to
prepare the chocolate mousse for dessert and the veal
Marsala and vegetables she planned for the main course.

She slipped away now and then to take a bath, put on
makeup and arrange her hair in between meal prepara-
tions. By the time she set the table, Dusty was cleaned,
shaved, dressed and wearing a path between the kitchen,
dining room and living room, popping his knuckles inces-
santly, and she was still in her robe with spiky electric
curlers in her hair. She had visions of C.J. Casey and the
president of Sunburst Records walking in on her this way.
At last, satisfied with the table arrangement, she hurried
to her room, tore the curlers out of her hair and brushed it
into its usual smooth chin-length cap. Next she opened the
louvered doors of her closet and gazed dismally at the
clothes hanging inside. There wasn't much to choose from,
so it shouldn't be hard to make up her mind, Cathleen
thought. The problem was, nothing pleased her. She
didn't have the right figure for slack suits, she thought, but
a dress was too formal for the occasion.

After a great deal of dithering and trying on three
different outfits, Cathleen decided to wear a pale lavender
gray three-piece pants suit, her most recent purchase. It
was fashionable and struck the correct balance between
specialness and informality. The slacks were trim and
tailored, with a wide waistband. The full-sleeved, boxy

white jacket had lavender piping around the collarless neck and lapels, and it hung open to reveal the lavender, scoop-necked blouse beneath. The blouse was the problem. If Cathleen discarded the jacket, the pantsuit presented a sexier image than she liked. Although the neckline dipped no lower than the top of her breasts, the blouse showed a great deal of flesh between its spaghetti straps. Worst of all, it was impossible to wear a bra with it. That fact combined with the tight waistband of the trousers served to emphasize her hourglass figure rather than tone it down.

Cathleen glanced at herself in the mirror and quickly put on the jacket. Without it, the outfit was too inviting to wear around C.J. Casey. She would have to keep the jacket on all evening. The doorbell rang as she slipped into her shoes. She sprayed on a shot of perfume and hurried down the hall to the front door. Dusty was there before her, opening the door with his most affable grin, all traces of his earlier nervousness vanished. "Hey, John, how you doing?" he questioned cheerfully, reaching out to shake hands. "And C.J. Casey, as I live and breathe." He shook hands with him, too, adding a friendly clap on the shoulder.

Cathleen sighed. She would never understand her father. Here he was, easily greeting two men whom he'd tried to punch out the last time he saw them. It wasn't that he was phony. In many ways Dusty was painfully honest. He just had a convenient memory, and his anger was over as soon as he roared, especially if he was drunk at the time he became enraged. He rarely held a grudge and was surprised that other people didn't forget his transgressions as easily as he forgot theirs.

Cathleen fixed a smile on her face and stepped forward. "Good evening, Mr. Metcalf." She extended her hand to the slim, graying man, and he shook it, although his stare was plainly blank. "I'm Cathleen, Dusty's younger daughter," she prodded.

"Cathleen!" A genuine smile crossed the man's face.

"Well, I'll be. I didn't recognize you. I still think of you as being about twelve years old."

"No, I grew up. Sorry," Cathleen joked.

"Don't be," Casey spoke up. "I'm rather glad you did."

Cathleen steeled herself to face him. "Hello, Casey." He looked sexier than he had the afternoon before. He wore a full-sleeved, dark blue satin shirt which deepened the blue of his eyes and exposed more of his brown throat and chest than Cathleen was comfortable seeing. The softness of the material and the wide sleeves were a perfect foil for his hard, masculine body and devilishly handsome face. His legs were encased in the usual tight-fitting jeans, although in honor of the occasion he had worn new designer jeans instead of his normal worn and faded denims. In a business known for its rich, flashy costumes, Casey stood out like a sore thumb. He had been known to appear on stage in an old navy blue T-shirt, scuffed boots and patched jeans. Legions of fans called his style of dressing natural and down to earth. Cathleen suspected it was part of his stage persona: the rebel, the outlaw, the singer of gritty hard-luck songs and sensual love ballads. Besides, the tight jeans and T-shirts showed off a body more worth showing than most. Whatever the reasons for his style of dress, Cathleen knew that what he had worn tonight represented dressing up, and it vaguely pleased her, though she couldn't imagine why she should care.

"Hello, Cathleen." The husky, warm voice curled around her caressingly, and the bright blue eyes held hers. "You're very pretty tonight."

"Thank you," she replied stiffly, embarrassed and frightened by his effect on her.

"Well, don't stand around out here in the hall. Come inside and sit down," Dusty urged, leading them into the living room.

Cathleen seized the opportunity to slip off to the kitchen and check the food. Everything was in order, but she lingered for a few minutes, delaying her return to the living room and bolstering her courage. It was an important evening for Dusty. She must not mess it up by reacting to Casey like a schoolgirl, first angry, then stammering and practically blushing. Surely she could spend an evening with the man without being rude, stiff or tongue-tied.

"Can I help?"

Cathleen whirled to see Casey leaning against the doorjamb, his arms crossed casually.

"What? Oh, no. I was about to dish up the food and put it on the table."

"I've been known to carry a bowl or two." He pushed himself away from the door frame and strolled toward her in the lazy, long-legged prowl that was another of his trademarks.

"I can't imagine C.J. Casey setting dishes on the table," Cathleen joked breathlessly.

He grinned. "How do you think I eat at home? Standing at the kitchen counter?"

Cathleen had to giggle. "No. I can't imagine you eating at home, either."

"Are you kidding? That's the only place I eat when I'm in Nashville. I get enough cafe food on tour. Even a TV dinner is delicious after some of the cardboard I've eaten in motel restaurants."

"TV dinners?" Cathleen repeated skeptically. "Come on, you can't make me believe *you* have to resort to TV dinners. Surely you must have maids and cooks."

"Of course. Hell, honey, you know the life as well as I do. I have a housekeeper who fixes lunch and cooks my dinner before she leaves for the day, but I keep a strange schedule. Sometimes I eat in the middle of the night instead of the end of the day. Then I have to resort to the microwave. Actually, I'm pretty good at fixing a few things—snacks, breakfasts. I'm a hell of a breakfast maker." The familiar mocking, downturned smile crossed his face. "You ought to try me sometime." The implications of eating one of his breakfasts were clear, and Cathleen glanced away.

"I'm afraid I don't need any help," she said, returning to his original question.

"Probably not, but I thought I'd give Dusty and John some time alone. If I know Dusty, he'll charm John into forgetting his last two albums."

"Oh. Sure." She wouldn't be able to get rid of him. Cathleen turned and opened one of the cabinets. Making a concerted effort not to let his presence bother her, she pulled out a serving bowl and platter and began to remove the food from the stove and put it into the containers. Casey ambled to the refrigerator and took out the salad dressing and butter, as if he lived there.

"You put this butter in one of those fancy little dishes?" he asked.

"What? Oh, uh, yes." She squatted to dig around in a low cabinet, unsettled by his ease in her kitchen. C.J. Casey, millionaire singer and the major villain of her life, shouldn't be so at home, so comfortable and ordinary. And light blue eyes shouldn't be so scorching. As she handed him the butter dish her fingers grazed his, and she snatched her hand back from the hot, rough feel of his skin.

He tilted his head to one side. "Hey, do I scare you or something?"

"Scare me?" Her mouth was dry and her attempt at laughter a dismal failure. "No. Should you?"

"I don't know. You seem awfully nervous."

"It's Dusty. Tonight is so important. I want everything to be exactly right," she lied. He did scare her—not because he might harm her, but because he stirred up irrational, conflicting feelings in her.

Casey shrugged. "There's only so much you can do. A gourmet meal won't get your dad a contract. John Metcalf is immune to being softened up with food or drink. It's up to Dusty and his songs. Dusty's handling himself well. He's in better shape than, well, I guess than any time since I've known him."

"I know, but it's hard not to worry." She turned back to

the counter, dismissing the subject. She carried the bowls of asparagus and hollandaise sauce into the dining room, and Casey followed with the salad. She managed to avoid eye contact and conversation by arranging the food on the table, but as she started back into the kitchen Casey caught her arms. She glanced up into his face, startled, and wished she hadn't. His heavy-lidded eyes gazed into hers, mesmerizing in their intensity.

"There's nothing left to bring in," he told her.

"Oh."

His hands didn't leave her arms. Instead they traveled up, leaving a trail of tingling flesh even though her jacket separated his hands from her skin. When he reached her shoulders he didn't stop, but kept on, sliding his hands to her throat and up to clasp her face, thumbs beside her chin and forefingers resting on her jaw in front of her ear. "You turned into a very pretty lady. That's why I wormed my way into the dinner invitation. I wanted to see you again."

Cathleen swallowed, unable to speak, heart-stoppingly aware of his callused fingertips against her skin and his eyes boring into hers. Softly his thumbs caressed her chin and cheeks, and he tilted her face up. Cathleen watched him as his face drew closer, her heart knocking painfully against her ribs. She couldn't move, could hardly breathe, held static by warring excitement and dread. His lips hovered over hers for a moment, and she closed her eyes in an unconscious gesture of surrender. He kissed her softly, barely brushing his lips over hers, but his very nearness made her tremble with rushing, clashing emotions. She breathed in the scent of his cologne, felt the gentle prickles of his beard against her flesh, was touched by the heat of his skin. His kiss teased her senses, bringing them to sudden, intense life.

Again his mouth pressed against hers, slow and hot, learning her lips and tongue and teeth. Casey's kiss was leisurely and expert, a moist, arousing exploration that filled Cathleen with sizzling heat. His hands slipped down to her back and pulled her against him, pressing her into the hard, angular lines of his body. His arms encircled her, lifting her to her tiptoes. Her breasts thrust against his chest, the nipples puckering at the contact. He slid his hands slowly over her ribs, delighting in the contrast of soft feminine flesh over hard bone structure.

The kiss ended, and Casey moved to nuzzle her ear and cheek, his beard brushing her skin. "Mmm, you smell good," he whispered in her ear. His tongue teased at the lobe. "Delicious." He rolled the tender skin between his lips. "Almost as good as you taste."

Cathleen quivered and wrapped her arms around his waist, her fingers digging into his back. Instinctively she turned her head, seeking his lips as he met her in a deep, lingering kiss. His mouth ground into hers, and his tongue swept into the warm, sweet cave, twining around her tongue in a seductive dance of invitation. Cathleen answered him with equal fervor, lost to the time and place. She knew only the fiery seeking of their tongues and the fierce joy of his arms crushing her to him. Casey's skin was suddenly blazing, and his hands dropped to her hips, pressing her up into him, imprinting her with his hard desire.

Casey uttered a low, wordless sound of frustration and tore his mouth away, reluctantly loosening his hold. "I wish Dusty and Metcalf weren't out there," he murmured, trying to smile and failing.

Cathleen crashed back to reality. She was standing in Casey's arms and had been kissing him with wild abandon! She stared at him in horror, then fled to the kitchen. Casey didn't follow her.

Cathleen ran through the kitchen and out the side door, emerging into the cool evening air. She stopped on the small concrete landing and gripped the metal railing, sucking in deep breaths. It was insane! She didn't understand how she could have allowed him to kiss her, let alone responded as eagerly as she had. As soon as Casey touched her, she lost all ability to think, and reacted with primitive passion. It was humiliating to have so little control over herself. Casey must be laughing at how easily she had fallen into his arms. Had he compared her lovemaking to her mother's?

She pressed her hands against her flaming cheeks. How could she face the others? Casey would flash her a knowing leer, and Dusty would ask her what was wrong. Cathleen swallowed, willing her turbulent emotions to subside. She had to go back inside. Dusty needed her. She had to pull herself together. She sucked in a few more deep, calming breaths and slipped into the kitchen. Peering into the window which, with the dark outside, served as a kind of mirror, she smoothed her hair and checked to make sure her lipstick wasn't smeared. Vaguely satisfied, she closed her eyes for a moment, marshaling her forces, then spun to march into the living room, a stiff smile fixed on her face.

"Supper's ready, everybody," she announced, avoiding Casey's eye.

"Great!" Dusty bounced up, and linked his arm with hers. "Come on, John, you're in for a real treat. My baby grew up to be quite a cook."

Cathleen managed to ignore Casey through most of the meal. He was silent, and Cathleen strove to cover his silence with pleasant chatter, hoping she wasn't making a complete idiot of herself. Her delicious meal could have been sawdust for all she tasted it, though Dusty and John praised it extravagantly. After dinner she cleared the table quickly, afraid Casey would offer to help. When he didn't, she was curiously deflated. Cathleen wiped her sweating palms on a dishtowel and walked into the living room. Dusty looked up and smiled, and John Metcalf nodded to her pleasantly. Casey studied her inscrutably.

"I told John you'd help your old man sing, honey," Dusty informed her jovially, "but I was beginning to think I'd have to drag you out of the kitchen."

"I'm nervous. Sorry."

"Please don't be, Cathleen," John Metcalf assured her. "We're friends here."

"Sure." Dusty picked up his guitar. "What do you want to play?"

"Piano." The fuller tones of the piano would better hide any slips or defects in Dusty's rendition. She sat down at the instrument and ran her fingers over the keys to limber them up. She wished she had thought about playing the piano when she had chosen this outfit. Any restrictions to her arms, even the loose sleeves of this jacket, bothered her. She ran a scale or two up and down and decided to slip off her jacket. After all, she wasn't scantily dressed. If Casey assumed she were trying to entice him, it was too bad.

She turned to her father and smiled to signify that she was ready, willing herself not to look at Casey to see what he thought of the blouse. Dusty smiled back. "How about doing 'Dreamer'?"

"Okay." She played the first few bars, and they began the soft, bittersweet ballad, her pure, strong soprano harmonizing with Dusty's tenor, years of singing together at home making them blend naturally.

John Metcalf straightened, his eyes suddenly alight with interest. Casey had shifted in his chair when Cathleen removed her jacket. Now he sat forward, resting his elbows on his knees, his chin on his clasped hands, and stared at her. Both men were too familiar with the music industry not to recognize the special quality of Cathleen's voice. It was stronger than her parents', but it also held an appealing mixture of Dusty's poignancy and Stella's sweetness. Her range was wider than either of theirs. It was a haunting, beautiful voice. To Casey it sounded of clear, crisp autumn days, of heartbreak and loneliness, of joy laced with bittersweet memories. To John Metcalf, it sounded of money.

When they finished Cathleen glanced at Casey without thinking and found him staring at her, his eyes glowing with a soft, dark warmth she had never seen there. She blinked, wondering what it meant, but then John Metcalf spoke, breaking the link between them, and she turned her head toward him.

"Beautiful! Dusty, you haven't lost it, and Cathleen,

why haven't I heard you before? A voice like that shouldn't be hiding out here. Should it, C.J.?"

"No," Casey agreed in his slow, husky voice. "Your voice is something special. Sing another one, Cathleen."

"Oh, no, really," she demurred.

"Come on, Cath," her father urged. "I'll sing 'Jewel in the Night'—that's another of Cathleen's songs, by the way—and then you can sing something."

"All right." She had to forget that Casey was watching her, and help Dusty.

Dusty sang the song she had written for him. It was one she had worked on long and hard, trying to fit it exactly to his vocal range and style. The words were a peculiar blend of romantic love and cynical reality, the love story of two losers who meet in a bar and hope to replenish their lost dreams with a newfound love. She watched Casey for his reaction as Dusty sang, and she was pleased to see that his attention was caught. So was John Metcalf's. The knot in her chest eased. Maybe it would work out.

She sang a solo when Dusty finished, accompanying herself on his guitar. She chose one of her first songs, 'Jody,' which she had realized later was too difficult for most singers. She had learned enough now to write for the singer, not herself. 'Jody' was a lilting, lyrical ballad of the joy and blind, eager hope of young love. Her voice swept over the difficult notes with ease, vaulting upward and falling down, then building to the strong climax. She stopped, her face flushed, and flashed the radiant smile that was peculiarly her own.

Casey smiled back at her, but his turned-down mouth and drooping eyes conveyed not happiness, but a kind of hunger. Cathleen wet her lips, her body alive and vibrating under his gaze. She moved quickly to the piano and led Dusty into one of his old songs. They followed with another right on its heels. Next Dusty sang two of the songs he had written recently. Each time John Metcalf was generous with his approval. Cathleen observed him as he watched Dusty sing, and she could almost see the wheels spinning in his head. That was a good sign. He wasn't a music enthusiast who would simply be enthralled with the music. If he liked something, he was thinking of recording plans and marketing approaches.

When Dusty finished his last song everyone applauded. Casey said, "I want to sing one with you, Cathleen."

Cathleen's eyes widened. This was something she hadn't anticipated, and she didn't like the idea at all. "No, please . . ." she began to decline.

Dusty, flush with his success, wouldn't hear of her refusing. "Come on, honey, I want to hear you two sing. Don't you, John?"

"Certainly." There was a speculative gleam in Metcalf's eye that Cathleen didn't like. However, she knew she was trapped again and agreed grudgingly.

Dusty handed Casey his guitar, and Casey moved to where Dusty had been sitting. "How about 'Stay with Me'?" he suggested. "Do you know it?"

"Sure." Cathleen had hated Casey for years, but the musical side of her couldn't help but appreciate his consummate artistry. She knew most of his songs by heart. She also knew that she didn't want to sing this one with him. It was his most sensual ballad, a slow, sad song of need and loneliness that touched the soul, yet stirred the senses in its evocation of hungry lovemaking.

Casey strummed a couple of chords and began in his gravelly voice:

> "Girl, don't leave me now
> Stay with me until the morning light."

Cathleen moved naturally into the next two lines:

> "And I will show you how
> To love away the dark and lonely night."

Casey chimed in on the chorus, their different voices—hers so clear and his so husky—mingling in an unexpected-

ly pleasant harmony. Her voice was beautiful and feminine, his the epitome of the tough, world-weary male. The
contrast was unique and stirring. Casey stared into her
eyes as he sang; Cathleen couldn't help but gaze back, held
captive by the music and his charisma. He sang the
suggestive lines to her, his eyes conveying everything the
words expressed and more. Cathleen was almost breathless under the impact of his melting voice and hot gaze.
She was afraid she would forget the words, but the lines
came to her easily, as though there was nothing else she
could say. When the song was over they sat for a moment,
gazes locked, until Dusty's exuberant voice broke the
spell.

"Fantastic!" he cried. "Baby, that was beautiful."

"Yes, it was. Very special," John Metcalf agreed more
quietly.

Casey said nothing, just glanced at her and then away.
Cathleen swallowed, unsure whether she could gather the
wits to respond. She mumbled something and moved away
from Casey. His eyes followed her. Nervously she turned.
"Could I get anyone anything?"

"No, thank you," John Metcalf answered. "We need to
be going. Dusty, I'll admit I was skeptical at first, but I'm
interested in another album from you. Have your agent
call me tomorrow. Is it still—"

"It's Eddy Lambert now," Cathleen cut in, naming her
boss. She was certain he'd be happy to represent Dusty.
She wasn't about to let Joe Siegel get anything out of this
deal, not after the way he'd rebuffed Dusty.

"Okay, have Eddy call me. I have an idea. Give me a
night to think about it. I'll get in touch with you."

"Sure. Sure, John." Dusty glowed.

The two men rose to leave. Casey clasped Dusty's hand
and gave him a wink and a smile. Then he turned to
Cathleen, and she linked her hands nervously behind her
back. His smile was knowing as he reached out to lightly
grasp her shoulders. For one wild moment she thought he
would pull her into his arms and kiss her, but he merely

bent and grazed his lips against her forehead. His breath was hot on her hair, his lips velvety. Cathleen couldn't suppress a shiver.

"Bye, darlin'." His voice was low and intimate. "We'll continue our conversation another time."

"Casey—"

He placed a forefinger on her lips and shook his head. "No arguments."

He followed Metcalf out the front door, leaving Cathleen staring after him helplessly. Dusty waved and closed the door, turning to his daughter with a huge grin. "Wasn't that great? Oh, honey, I owe it all to you." He swept her up in a bone-cracking hug. "Baby, things are going to be the way they were. I promise."

Cathleen summoned up a weak smile. "I hope so." She had the awful feeling that, for better or worse, her life had changed irrevocably.

Chapter 4

CATHLEEN HAD JUST HAMMERED OUT AN ERROR IN THE NEW Orleans hotel reservation for Jack's next tour when the phone rang. "Eddy Lambert Agency, Cathleen Richards speaking," she answered smoothly.

Eddy's elated voice burst in on her eardrums. "Guess what? We just signed a deal for you and Dusty!"

"*Me* and Dusty?" she repeated, stunned.

"Yeah, isn't it great? It appears I'll have to start looking for a new secretary. I have to run by your house and give Dusty the good news. Then I'll get back to the office and explain the whole deal to you. Have there been any phone calls?"

"Nothing that can't wait. But, Eddy . . ."

"Terrific. I gotta run. Bye."

Cathleen was left clutching the receiver. With a sigh, she replaced it. Her and Dusty? Eddy had specifically said that the deal was for both of them. But why? What did he mean? Was Dusty going to sing some of her songs? Surely that was what Eddy meant. Still . . . there was a nasty little fear inside her that it wasn't what he had meant at all.

Her fears were confirmed an hour later when Eddy

returned and informed her that John Metcalf wanted to sign a contract for an album on which both Dusty and Cathleen would sing. "He has a terrific promotional idea. He wants to call the album something like *Reunion* or *Old Friends*, and include other stars to boost its sales. A lot of the younger buyers hardly know Dusty's name. I told him Jack would sing a song with Dusty, and C.J. Casey's already agreed. John wants you to do a solo and a couple of songs with Dusty."

"Why me?" Cathleen cried. "I don't have a name to help sell the album."

"Because you have a beautiful voice. Why didn't you tell me? Metcalf practically gushed about it. Dusty'll sell to his old fans, and the others will bring in a lot of sales, but *you're* going to make the album popular. That's Metcalf's theory. You sound good with Dusty, he said. It's a special kind of harmony that relatives have, like the Gatlins, or the Carter family. You blend well with him, and you have a strong voice to carry him along and cover the rough spots. Dusty's voice isn't as good as it used to be."

"He's supposed to be rough-sounding. Lots of male stars are."

"Sure, but it doesn't hurt to help him out a little. What's the matter, Cathleen? You sound like somebody's trying to cheat you. Most people in this town would be jumping up and down with joy to hear this."

"I know. And I wish someone else were. *I don't want to record!*"

Lambert sank into a chair with a moan. "Lord, why me? The people in this business are going to drive me crazy! How can you not want to record? Everybody wants to record!"

"Not me. I want to be a songwriter. Period. So tell John Metcalf I don't want it."

Eddy sprang to his feet. "What?" he shrieked. "You must be crazy! I can't do that. We're talking big money here. Metcalf wants a banquet to mark Dusty's return to the music business. Dusty will be on talk shows to discuss his fight with alcoholism. Sunburst is planning to publicize and push the album. You'll throw away the chance of a lifetime."

"How many times do I have to say it?" Cathleen snapped back. "I don't want 'the chance of a lifetime.' Let them do it for Dusty alone."

Eddy rubbed one hand across his face and sighed. "They won't do it for just Dusty. You're part of the deal."

"Dusty will be fine without me."

"Metcalf wants you! If you don't record, the deal's off. Don't you understand? Metcalf heard you sing and knew he'd stumbled onto something great. He tried to hide how eager he was to sign you, but it was obvious. He thinks you'll be as big a star as Stella or Dusty, and he wants to get his hands on you before anyone else does. He might take a chance on Dusty, but it wouldn't be this kind of deal. He's priming you for stardom."

Cathleen stared at him levelly. "In other words, he's forcing me to sign. He's using Dusty to pressure me. Right?"

"I doubt he thought of it that way. Anybody else would jump at the opportunity he's offered you. To Metcalf, it's a way to kill two birds with one stone. For one album's publicity he gets Dusty's career rekindled and yours started. This album will help *both* you and Dusty, especially with someone like C.J. Casey volunteering to be on it. It's not worth the investment to do it for Dusty alone, because who knows how long it will be until Dusty's back to his old ways?"

He won't go back to his old ways!" Cathleen flared. "He's over that."

"I hope so. But you don't risk big bucks on wishful thinking."

Cathleen opened her mouth to argue, but shut it with a snap. "Oh, all right! I'll do it. But only because of Dusty and only this one album. Understood?"

"Understood." Eddy grinned, his florid, heavy face lighting up. "That's my girl. Whew! I never had a conversation like that one—persuading a client to accept her first album contract."

Cathleen frowned, ignoring his comment. "Eddy, did you say Casey had already agreed to sing on the album?"

"Yeah, apparently they discussed it last night on the way home from your house."

"I'll just bet they did," Cathleen murmured grimly.

"What?"

"Nothing." She was sure that Casey had set up the deal. She didn't know why he was pursuing her. Perhaps it offered some sort of titillation to his jaded sexual appetite to seduce the daughter of a woman he had made love to. Or it could be the challenge of taking away Dusty's daughter as well as his wife. Perhaps he resented Dusty, who had been powerful when Casey was first trying to break into show business. Whatever the reason, Casey had wanted to make love to her, and now he was trying to buy her gratitude with a recording contract. Cathleen's mouth twisted into a grimace. C.J. Casey had a surprise coming. Not only was she not grateful, it made her dislike him even more.

Eddy returned to his office, shaking his head. Cathleen forced herself to sit down at her desk and continue her work. However, she couldn't concentrate. Her mind kept going to her father and the album and C.J. Casey, excitement mingling with anger. Finally she gave up work as a lost cause and asked Eddy if she could leave early. Glad to see her exhibit a spark of excitement about the album, he expansively waved her home.

Cathleen drove to the small house, expecting to be met at the door by Dusty, his arms open for a bone-crushing congratulatory hug. Instead she found a note saying he'd gone to celebrate with Jack. Icy fear stabbed her stomach. Celebrate—that meant a drink. Hurriedly she pushed away the thought. No. Jack wouldn't let Dusty drink with him. She had to stop suspecting Dusty and fearing a return to his old ways every time he was out of her sight. It would drive him straight back to the bottle.

She went into the living room and slumped down on the sofa, staring sightlessly out the window. She hadn't wanted to make the album, had been mad and unwilling when

Eddy told her, but now she was curiously deflated that Dusty had gone out to celebrate without her. Of course, he hadn't known she would come home early, or he might have waited. Again she stopped herself. If Dusty were cured, they would start living separate lives. They would no longer be in the mutual prison shared by an alcoholic and his keeper. Cathleen was looking forward to her freedom. She must let Dusty have his, too.

With a sigh, Cathleen rose and strolled into her bedroom, where she slipped out of her working dress and pulled on comfortable jeans and a dusky rose cotton blouse. She splashed her face with water and ran a brush through her hair, then went into the kitchen. She popped the top off a can of diet soda and sat down at the old kitchen table to read a magazine, propping her feet up on another chair. Idly she flipped through the pages of fashion, articles and recipes as she mentally considered her supper possibilities. However, she couldn't keep her thoughts trained on such mundane things. Her mind kept slipping back to Casey and his disturbing kisses—and her even more disturbing reaction to them. It appalled her that she could be so affected by a man whom she had despised for years. There must be some fundamental weakness in her character for her to respond to him the way she had. Could it be that she was like her mother? Did her body rule her head and heart?

It was a relief when her thoughts were interrupted by the harsh singsong of the doorbell. She opened the front door to find Casey standing on the porch. Cathleen's first reaction was to slam the door in his face. He was too compelling and troubling. She had to face him sooner or later, though, and now, when she was still flushed with anger, would be the best time. She would let him know in no uncertain terms how she felt about his machinations. She braced her hands on her hips, blue eyes flashing. "You have a lot of nerve!"

He looked amused. "So I've been told. What in specific prompted you to say it?"

"As if you didn't know."

"Let's pretend I don't."

"You persuaded John Metcalf to put me on the album, didn't you? While you were driving home last night, you suggested that you'd be happy to sing on Dusty's album if they gave me a couple of songs, too."

His eyes widened in genuine surprise. "That would make you mad?"

"Yes! I don't want to cut an album."

He shook his head. "I knew you were unique. Could we discuss this inside, or do you intend to keep me standing on the doorstep?"

Cathleen stepped aside with a notable lack of graciousness. Casey passed her and walked into the den with all the ease of a frequent and welcome visitor, which irritated Cathleen further. He acted at home anywhere, shacks or palaces, among friends or enemies. Once she had thought it one of his more appealing qualities. Now she knew it was simply an expression of his enormous ego and essential callousness.

Casey settled into an easy chair near the back window and crossed his legs, one foot propped on the other knee and a hand resting lightly atop his ankle. He squinted up at her with a wry expression. "Okay, shoot. I take it you think I was so nefarious and scheming as to help you get your first album."

Put that way, it sounded ridiculous. Most people would have been grateful. "You did it to put me in your debt!" she blurted out, knowing even as she said it that it would earn her a knowing smile from Casey.

"You mean I figured you'd be so grateful you'd run to my bed?" he asked, his gravelly voice laced with laughter yet managing to sound infinitely seductive as well.

Cathleen blushed. "I'm sure that's the sort of woman you're used to dealing with."

His amusement deepened. "The only way I can get a woman to sleep with me is to pay her off with a record contract?"

Furiously aware that she was digging herself in deeper

and deeper, Cathleen spat, "You're the most infuriating person I know!"

He laughed. "I'm sorry. Do you mind my teasing? Face it, Cath, you left yourself open for it. I came here to ask you out for a celebration dinner, but obviously I'll have to straighten out this problem first. To begin with, I don't pay, bribe, blackmail or inveigle women to sleep with me. I've gotten too old for sex without feeling. Secondly, I didn't persuade John to sign you for the album. He told me his idea for the album and asked if I'd sing on it. I said sure. Then he asked me what I thought of you. I told him the truth—that you have one of the best voices I've heard. He said he wanted to sign you to Sunburst, and I said he'd be crazy if he didn't. I don't lie about music, darlin', not even to help someone I like."

Cathleen glared at him. She had the awful feeling that he was telling the truth and that she had made a fool of herself. It had been presumptuous to think that Casey, who could have any woman he wanted, would go to such trouble to get *her*. Besides, she knew enough about music to realize that her voice was good, and enough about the music industry to understand Metcalf's reasoning. Casey wouldn't have had to urge him to sign her. Metcalf had already had the gleam of dollar signs in his eyes as she sang. "Okay. I was out of line," she admitted in a low voice, keeping her eyes turned away from his. "I'm sorry. Oh, damn!" She sank down into the nearest chair. "Now I don't have anyone to be mad at!"

Again Casey laughed. "Careful, Cath. Honesty can get you into trouble." He leaned forward, his azure eyes bright with amusement. "I'll volunteer to be your punching bag if you need one."

"I don't want to do it!" Cathleen punctuated her words by hitting her fist against her knee.

"Then don't. Tell him no."

"That's what I told Eddy." A faint smile touched her lips as she remembered the agent's horrified expression. "You'd have thought I'd asked him to jump off a bridge."

"Lambert would probably enjoy it more. But surely you aren't singing because Eddy Lambert would be upset."

"No, of course not. Eddy said Metcalf wouldn't want Dusty if I didn't sing." She swiveled to look at him. "Is that true?"

Casey shrugged and leaned back in his chair. He placed his elbows on the arms of the chair and formed a steeple with his fingers, its apex resting on his lips. Cathleen's eyes were drawn to his hands, so long and slender, yet saved from delicacy by their browned, corded strength. The tips were callused from years of guitar playing. She remembered their faint roughness on the skin of her face. Guiltily she jerked her mind away from the thought and made herself listen to what he was saying.

"Frankly, darlin', I don't know if Metcalf would take Dusty without you. He has reservations about your father. John's memory is like an elephant's, especially where profit-and-loss statements are concerned. I think he could forget the time Dusty tried to knock him down, but not those dismal sales on his last album. Face it, Dusty sounded like hell. His songs were flat and boring. They went over budget, and the album was so poorly received it didn't break even. Everybody has a poor record now and then, but Dusty's was the last in a string of them. His sales went lower with each album. Fans are only so loyal."

"I know." She sighed. "Eddy doesn't think Metcalf will take him back unless I sing, so I agreed."

"Then you will record the album?"

"Yes."

He smiled. "I'm glad. You're too good to waste." His lazy smile gave the words an added meaning. Cathleen flushed and looked away. "Now, how about dinner?"

"Dusty's not here."

"I wasn't asking Dusty."

Cathleen's chin jutted out. "*I* have nothing to celebrate."

"We'll make it a wake, then."

She flashed him a speaking glance. "Obviously you have

to be hit over the head with it: I don't want to go out with you. Anywhere. Anytime."

"That seems to cover it." Casey frowned and went to her. He squatted down to take her hands in his. "Sweetheart, what's the problem? Whenever I'm around you run like a scared rabbit. You put your head down and refuse to look at me, or you look out in the distance as if I don't exist. Do I frighten you? Do you think of me as being your father's age and a dirty old man?"

"Don't be silly," she snapped, trying unsuccessfully to tug her hands from his grasp. "I know you're years and years younger than Dusty. You're only thirty-something."

"Three," he supplied. "Do I scare you? I know it can't be that you don't feel the chemistry between us." He grinned wickedly, raising one of her hands to his lips and softly kissing the back of it. His lips were velvety against her skin, teasing, promising.

"There isn't any chemistry between us," Cathleen denied.

He chuckled. "Liar." He turned her hand over and nuzzled the palm. Hot shivers darted up her arm as she tried desperately to pull her hand away. Casey held it firmly as his lips wandered up to the delicate, blue-veined skin of her inner wrist, evoking the same tingling, erotic sensations.

Cathleen closed her eyes. She didn't know how to handle this. "Casey, no." It was almost a moan.

He sat down on the floor, gently pulling her out of the chair and down with him. "Baby, don't be scared of me. I wouldn't hurt you for the world." He let go of her hands, but she was more caught than ever, for he settled her into his arms, bending one knee to support her against his leg. Cathleen felt encircled, trapped by his hard body although his hold was loose. He kissed her neck where it flowed into her shoulders, burrowing his face into her flesh.

One hand slipped down to cup her breast, igniting more sparkling shivers throughout her body. His thumb moved over the soft mound, her blouse little impediment to his exploration, and circled her nipple until it pouted visibly through the material. He began to kiss her slowly, warm lips moving across her neck and face, planting languid kisses upon her skin, until finally he reached her mouth. His lips settled on hers, first lightly, the barest warm breath of a movement, then coming back to taste the full riches of her mouth. Though Cathleen struggled not to open to him, she was incapable of denying his insistent mouth. His tongue teased her lips open and slipped inside, caressing the roof of her mouth with its pliant heat.

He pulled away only to change the slant of their kiss. His mouth was greedy on hers as his agile fingers unbuttoned her blouse and caressed her breasts. The hard buttons of her nipples thrust out shamelessly against the thin material of her bra, and he took one between his forefinger and thumb, rolling it until it stretched and hardened even more, aching for his touch. His breath rasped against her cheek, and his other arm tightened around her.

Casey lay down on the floor, taking Cathleen with him, and rolled over so that she lay on her back, his long body stretched out half on top of her. Their mouths clung, Cathleen no more willing to break the seal than he was. His hands roamed her body, stroking her abdomen and thighs and returning again and again to her lush breasts. He broke away from her mouth to rain tiny, feather-light kisses over her face and neck. His lips toyed with her ears, first one and then the other, nibbling, circling, flicking and finally invading with his warm, wet tongue. Cathleen groaned at the exquisite pleasure. It was her own animal sound of hunger that snapped her out of the fog of sensations in which she had been floating.

"Casey, no," she mumbled, squirming away from him. For a moment he held her, but when she shoved against him, he opened his arms and released her.

"Oh, Cathleen," he groaned, sitting up in a jackknife position, arms crossed on his knees. He dropped his forehead onto his arms and rolled it against the cool silk of his shirt. "Honey, what are you trying to do to me?"

"Me!" she burst out. "Me trying to do something to you? Of all the unmitigated gall! C.J. Casey, you're a sneaky, underhanded . . ." She couldn't think of anything loathsome enough to express her feelings.

"Varmint?" he suggested, squinting up at her, humor glinting in his eyes. "You sound like a grade-B western."

"Well, I'm glad you're amused!"

"Frustrated is more like it," he snapped back, and rose lithely to his feet. "Cathleen, I'm trying to be as decent as it's possible for me to be, but . . ."

"I'm sure it's a great effort for you."

"Why in the hell do you melt when I kiss you, then the next minute jump away and act as if I'd tried to rape you? Why do you carry this chip on your shoulder with me?"

"How can you ask that? It disgusts me that I let you kiss me. I despise you. Any man who would do what you did to Dusty, after all the help he'd given you, is the lowest kind of person. You're a snake."

"Exactly *what* did I do to Dusty?" His face was suddenly tight, his blue eyes bright and cold. "You mean he didn't want this record contract either? Or do you mean ten years ago, when I stopped putting up with his crazy jealousies and insults and foul temper?"

"I mean ten years ago when you had an affair with his wife!"

He gaped at her for a moment, then unexpectedly burst into laughter.

His laughter was a spark to the tinder of her raw, seething emotions. "Get out of this house! I-I hate you! I—oh—" She whirled and ran from him, tears welling up in her eyes. The last thing she wanted was for Casey to see her cry over him.

He caught up with her before she reached the hall, one hand clamping around her wrist like iron and whirling her around to face him. "Damn it, Cathy, don't run out without giving me a chance to explain."

"Explain! What can you explain? Why it still amuses you that you wrecked so many lives and destroyed the man who gave you your career? All for the sake of your own selfish pleasure!"

"You little idiot." He grasped her by the shoulders and shook her lightly, the look on his face revealing a desire to shake her harder. "Did you actually believe Dusty's drunken ravings? I thought you had more sense, even when you were a teenager."

"Are you claiming you didn't sleep with Stella?" Cathleen challenged heatedly.

"I never touched your mother! My God, how can you be so gullible? Dusty'll lie like a dog when he's drunk. You ought to know that. Hell, I don't think he even knows whether or not he's telling the truth when he's knee-crawling drunk, which is what he was for over nine years."

"Don't you dare talk that way about him! You did it to him."

"I did nothing to him, except put up with a lot of things anybody in their right mind wouldn't have. That day on your front porch wasn't the first time he took a swing at me. He was just lucky enough to connect, for once. For about six months before Stella left him, whenever he got drunk he'd accuse me of sleeping with her and try to pick a fight. He'd tell me over and over that I was riding on his coat tails. He'd say I'd be nothing without him. I was a born loser."

He dropped his hands and swung away from her, his hands balling into fists. "I loved that man, Cathy. I really did. Sometimes I thought of him as a father. He did so much for me. I could talk to him like I never could to my own father. He was kind and generous at first. He loved music. We could sit around picking our guitars and singing and talking for hours. Then he turned on me. I never knew what happened. Suddenly he started sniping at me, making snide remarks, accusing me . . . accusing me. . . ."

Casey sighed and rubbed his face, then ran his hands up through his hair. The taut emotions drained from him and he turned back to Cathleen. For a long moment they stared at each other in silence. Cathleen was shaken by the force of his raw feelings. Truth was stamped all over him—his posture, the intensity of his gaze, the ring of pain in his words. But she made one last effort to return things to the way she had always thought of them. "I saw the way you looked at Stella. You loved her."

"Yeah." He released another long breath. "I loved Stella. She was beautiful, desirable and fun. Her voice could touch you right where it hurt. Oh, hell, she could be bitchy and selfish and a real pain in the rear, too, but I ignored those things. I was too dazzled."

His words pierced Cathleen, taking away her breath and bringing stinging tears to her eyes. Why did it hurt so much to hear him confess that he'd loved her mother? She'd known it for a long time.

"But," Casey continued firmly, "I didn't try anything with her. I never so much as kissed her, let alone had an affair with her. No matter how much I wanted Stella, I couldn't betray Dusty. He'd done too much for me. Obviously you find it hard to believe, but I do have principles."

Cathleen closed her eyes, suddenly sick to her stomach. Her world was tilting and sliding away from her. Dusty had lied, as he had about so many things. Casey was another one of his victims, someone upon whom he had vented his strange, wild rage. She knew it deep in the pit of her stomach. Shakily she turned away, trying to formulate words to deal with this new knowledge.

Casey watched her, seeing her quiet, cold face and the stubborn set of her jaw. "You don't want to admit it, do you?" he demanded. "You'd rather think someone else wrecked Dusty's life. Let me tell you, honey, Dusty and Stella didn't need any help to ruin their marriage. They did it real well by themselves." He paused for a moment and glanced at her wooden face. "I think I better go."

She turned her wide eyes toward him, soft and brimming with tears. "Yes, please. I . . . need to be by myself, I think."

The twisted ghost of a smile touched his lips. "Keep your dreams, Cathleen. Good-bye."

Chapter 5

FOR A LONG TIME AFTER CASEY LEFT, CATHLEEN REMAINED IN a chair, digesting what he had told her. It had to be the truth. No one could lie that convincingly. How could she have been so naive? She would have said that after a lifetime with Dusty she had no illusions left. Yet she had clung to her father's story as fiercely as if it were her own. An ache started deep in her chest.

All these years, she'd hated Casey for no reason. She could have spared herself the churning anger and resentment. She had lashed out at him, snubbed him, avoided him—and she'd been wrong. It was galling. It hurt. It was as if she'd been deprived of something, although she couldn't say exactly what. But if she *had* been deprived, it had been she herself who did it. She recalled Lynette's suggestion that Cathleen's teenage crush on Casey had caused her to react irrationally. Was that the reason? Had she been crushed more because Casey loved another woman than because he had betrayed her father? Had she lashed out at him in jealousy? Or had she simply been looking for a scapegoat, and Casey had been handy?

The sound of the kitchen door closing interrupted her thoughts, and Cathleen rose, recognizing her father's familiar steps. For a moment she panicked, certain that she wouldn't be able to face him. But no, she couldn't blame Dusty. The fault was all hers. She'd believed Dusty, despite knowing how he lied when he was drunk. Dusty strode into the hall and glanced into the den. When he saw her he stopped, and a wide grin lit his face. "Cathleen, come here and give your old man a hug. We're back in business!"

"You're back in business," Cathleen contradicted good-humoredly. "Unfortunately, I'm starting out."

"Ah, it won't be any time till you're one of the biggest. I have an eye for those things, you know. Look at the way I picked out Stella and Casey."

Cathleen ignored his first statement. She wouldn't spoil Dusty's happiness by complaining that she didn't want to make a record. "Daddy, speaking of Casey . . ."

"Yeah?" He sauntered into the room and hugged her when she made no move to come to him. Then he drew back and stared into her eyes, frowning. "Is something the matter? Did Casey upset you?"

"No, no. That is . . . Casey did come by, and we talked. Daddy, I have to ask you a question. I hope it won't upset you."

He shrugged. "The doctors say I have to learn to cope. Shoot."

"When Stella left, you told me it was because she was having an affair with Casey. Was that true?"

Dusty dropped into a chair, emitting a long sigh. "At the time, I thought so. I couldn't bear to lose Stella, and I didn't want to admit that she left because I was a lousy husband and a drunk. I could see Casey had the hots for her, and I knew Stella well enough to know she wouldn't refuse him. I decided they were having an affair. I *wanted* to think that was why Stella left me." He glanced up, guilt in his eyes. "But it wasn't true. Casey was too loyal. He put up with a lot from me and never said a word. He wouldn't have tried anything with my wife. Stella told me there was nothing between them and, whatever else she did, she didn't lie. She admitted the other men."

"Then why did you tell me they were having an affair?" Cathleen burst out.

Dusty shook his head. "I don't know. I was crazy back then, honey. I was scared I might lose you, that you would realize I was to blame for the divorce. Besides, in my warped way of thinking, I really believed it. Casey and Stella having an affair took care of everything. I could blame them, and I could get you to blame them, too. I'm sorry, honey. I shouldn't have. That's why you've cut yourself off from your mother, and it's my fault."

"No, Daddy," Cathleen said softly, going to kneel beside his chair and taking one of his hands in hers. "It wasn't your fault. Your story didn't change my relationship with Stella. We were never close. You know that. Lynette was Mama's girl, and I was your girl. Stella left us, and that's what I can't forgive her."

Dusty smiled tentatively. "Thanks, baby. You're sweet. Always were. I remember the first time you smiled at me, when you were just a baby. I knew then that you were the best thing ever happened to me. And look at how I've messed up your life."

Cathleen's stomach twisted and she rose, retreating a little. "That's not true, Dusty."

"Now, don't get upset. I'm not maudlin and self-recriminating like when I was drunk. Really, Cath. I'm not slipping back into it."

"Of course not." She summoned up a false smile. His words had scared her, reminding her too vividly of the nights when Dusty had cried repentant tears, full of beery remorse, and promised to reform, castigating himself for ruining her life. Those times had been almost as hard as when he smashed up furniture or stormed at her in rage.

"But I have to face facts," Dusty continued. "You've wasted a bunch of years on me. You should have been out having fun, dating, doing all the things other kids do, not riding herd on your drunken father."

"I chose to do it."

"I know. You're a sweet, darling girl. But I'm glad John wants you to sing on this album." He reached out a hand to her, smiling the brilliant smile that had swept more women under his spell than Cathleen cared to count. She couldn't help but return his grin. Dusty pulled her down onto the arm of his chair, retaining possession of her hand. "Finally I can give something back to you. Your career can go off like a skyrocket with this album."

"I don't really want a singing career," she interrupted mildly.

"Don't be crazy. With your voice? You have to sing. You know what I predict? You'll be a bigger star than your old man ever was—or Stella, either. The first time I saw you, I wanted to give you the world. I couldn't, but now your voice can." Cathleen gazed down at him, a sodden lump forming in her throat. Dusty looked different, serious and sad, as if he'd finally lost his ability to pretend. "Your voice reminds me of Mama. She could sing! She was the mainstay of the Pursey First Baptist Church choir—hell, most of them couldn't carry a tune."

Cathleen giggled. "I didn't know your mother sang. In fact, I don't know anything about your parents. You never took us to see them, either."

"Mama died before I left home, and the old man, well, I didn't care whether I saw him again. Mama was nice, but strict, you know. A real upright Christian lady. It nearly broke her heart the first time I got drunk. I was fifteen. Fell down staggering up our back steps and busted my guitar to pieces." He shook his head, the faint smile on his lips at odds with the infinite sorrow in his eyes. "Lord, did she ring a peal over my head. I was sick as a dog, and she strapped me something fierce, to boot. She died a year later, scared out of her mind because she was leaving me in my father's hands. She was afraid he'd let me go straight to hell."

"And did he?"

"Of course. She knew Dad pretty well. I turned out a lot like him, except he was meaner when he drank. I wanted him to talk to me and play with me when I was little, but he was too drunk all the time. I remember thinking: I'm going to love my kids and talk to them and sing to them. I planned to be a real good Daddy. So much for good intentions."

"You *were* a good father," Cathleen protested. "Who else but Lynette or I got to appear on the Grand Ole Opry when they were three years old? And who else had a daddy who sang them to sleep every night?"

"When I was home," he amended. "And when I wasn't drunk."

"Even when you were drunk, you sang to us. And we knew you loved us, no matter what happened." Cathleen circled his shoulders with one arm and leaned her head against his. Dusty's memories of his childhood tugged at her heart. "I love you, Daddy."

"I love you, pumpkin." Dusty's voice was thick with tears. He swallowed and smiled. "What are we doing swapping sad stories? This should be the happiest night of our lives." He rose and pulled her to her feet. "Feels kind of weird, having something to celebrate and not going out honky-tonking." He grinned and held up an imaginary glass. "Here's to our success."

Dusty tilted back the invisible glass and guzzled down its contents, finishing with a loud "ahhh." Cathleen imitated him, raising her cupped hand in the air. "To our success."

It was almost a month before Cathleen saw Casey again. The more she thought about how she had wronged him for so long, the more ashamed she was. She knew she ought to apologize to him, but every time she started to call, her courage faltered. She was embarrassed by her stubborn misbelief and sure that he regarded her with contempt. What if he hung up on her, or laughed at her stupidity?

Besides, she was better off leaving their relationship as it was. C.J. Casey was out of her league. He was rich, sophisticated, experienced, the sort of man who'd been everywhere and done everything at least twice. Cathleen wasn't awed by the wealthy trappings of his life, having grown up with them herself, but she feared his sexual experience. He could easily bring her to his bed and just as easily hurt her. He was used to casual affairs and no doubt only looking for fun, but Cathleen feared that she would wind up heartbroken if she got involved with him.

He was simply more than she could handle: too compelling and handsome, too involved with the country and western industry. In fact, he was altogether too much like her father. Their public images were much the same: hard-drinking, hard-fighting, hard-loving men. Heaven knew, it was an image that permeated country and western music, but it fit Casey better than most. He had been one of her father's best drinking buddies before their fight. And though he hadn't gone to bed with Stella, it was one of the few opportunities he had missed. He'd never qualified as a born hell-raiser, as Dusty had, because he didn't share Dusty's attraction to trouble. But Casey had been acclaimed as a premier ladies' man, constantly besieged by female fans and stars alike—and not prone to turn them down. When his brief marriage had broken up a few years ago, everyone had speculated that it was "woman trouble."

Casey was a charmer. Cathleen knew firsthand the power of his heady kisses. But it meant heartbreak to love a man like that. She was doubly susceptible to him because he was so much like Dusty. The best thing was to stay away from him. Casey was obviously through with her, and there was no sense in bringing herself to his attention again by phoning him to apologize. He would think she was willing to pick up where they left off.

Sooner or later she would run into him at the studios, and then would be the best time to apologize. However, despite her resolution, she couldn't seem to shake loose from the memory of him. She found herself thinking about Casey—his smile, his low chuckle, his long, sensitive fingers—and a warm glow would start in her chest. Why hadn't she had handled it differently? Why had she been so quick to judge, so harsh? Maybe something wonderful could have happened between them. Maybe . . .

Cathleen continued to work at Eddy's office until he

could find someone to replace her. In a way, she hated to
give up the job. Besides providing her with security, it was
an interesting place to work. Negotiating contracts with
the record companies was only part of Eddie's job as an
agent. He also arranged for public appearances, made
bookings for tours and provided the light and sound setups
for the artists. Since Eddy preferred to handle negotia-
tions and personal contacts, Cathleen was often left with
the detail work such as travel arrangements and hotel
reservations. Her work could be a headache, particularly
when one of Eddy's clients had a "special needs" rider in
his contract, requiring that certain foods or drinks or other
things be available at each stop. But at least the job was
never dull.

However, after she and Dusty signed their contracts
with Sunburst Records, which meant they were soon to
receive an advance on their royalties, there was no longer
a pressing financial reason for her to work. She needed to
be free to help Dusty with the final touches on arrangements, rehearse with him and record. So she left her job
with Eddie after two weeks and concentrated full-time on
her songwriting. She polished up several tunes and wrote
several new ones, hopeful that if the songs of hers that
Dusty did became hits she would be able to sell some of
her others. As the days passed, she grew more and more
excited about her unexpected opportunity to record.
There was something frightening and yet inviting about
the prospect of cutting a record. Although she had grown
up in the record business, she wasn't entirely immune to its
appeal, and once the initial shock had passed she realized
that the chance of a lifetime had dropped into her lap. She
could understand everyone else's amazement when she
had strongly opposed the offer. She still didn't like the idea
of singing on the album with Dusty, but she knew it would
be good for her songwriting career—and, after all, she
wouldn't have to continue to record if she didn't want to.

Within a month they were ready to record. John Metcalf
didn't want to waste time in getting out the records, since

the promotion was keyed to Dusty's fight against alcoholism and his release from the treatment center. The more
time that lapsed after his release, the less effective the
promotion became. Cathleen drove Dusty to the recording
studio the first day he was supposed to sing, feeling almost
as nervous as he was. When he jumped out of the car his
face was pale, and he flashed her an uncertain grin. But
when she returned to pick him up three hours later Dusty
was flushed, smiling and eager to talk about his marvelous
session. Cathleen beamed as she listened to him. Dusty
was back where he belonged, doing what he loved. She
knew she couldn't ask more than that. Guilt gave her heart
a squeeze as she thought that Dusty had this chance only
because of Casey's efforts. From her new perspective,
Casey's actions seemed very generous, considering the
hurt her father had inflicted on him.

The advance checks arrived that afternoon, and Dusty
promptly bought a car. Cathleen knew they needed another car, but her father would have nothing less than a
luxury sedan, and it made her wince to see him toss away
so much money in one shot. Unlike most country and
western stars, for whom the Mercedes Benz was the new
status automobile, Dusty preferred a large American car
like he had owned in his glory years. Next he began to buy
costumes for the tour Eddie was setting up, and he urged
her to do the same. In almost the same breath he talked of
ordering a custom-outfitted tour bus, the cost of which
could run into hundreds of thousands of dollars. It took all
her powers of persuasion to convince him to rent a used
bus from another singer. Cathleen knew she would have to
buy clothes for the inevitable public appearances and stage
shows, but she was determined to set the rest of her money
aside for a rainy day. Dusty might have licked his drinking
problem, but he obviously still had the spending habit.

Two days later they drove to Sunburst Records in their
new pale blue Cadillac. Cathleen slid out of the passenger
side and surreptitiously wiped her hands down the sides of
her jeans. It was her first appointment to record, and her

palms were sweaty with fear. A strange excitement swelled
in her throat, stifling her breath, and Cathleen feared she
wouldn't have the air to sing. A myriad of possible
disasters floated before her mind's eye. With a stiff smile
she took Dusty's arm, and they walked up the wide
concrete pathway to the Sunburst building.

Inside they passed the receptionist's desk and continued
down the long central hall to Studio C. The door to the
recording studio stood open, and two men lounged beside
it, smoking. Each raised a hand in lazy greeting to Dusty,
who stopped and introduced them to Cathleen. They were
two of the studio musicians who had been hired to play
backup. Dusty guided Cathleen inside the room, where
several other men sat or stood, conversing in loose groups.

Cathleen knew three of the men in the room. Two were
members of Dusty's old band, which he had tried to
reunite without great success. Only Jim Sargent and Vern
Holscher had not found other jobs too good to quit for a
comeback try. Although the men were good musicians,
Cathleen wished her father hadn't hired them. Dusty
would do better without anything or anybody to remind
him of the past. Jim was an easygoing guy who was unable
to refuse a favor or dissuade a friend from doing something harmful. Vern was worse. He was a drinker, one of
the buddies who had made the rounds with Dusty in the
old days. He was able to control himself better than Dusty
had ever done, but boozing was part of his way of life.
Cathleen feared that he would encourage Dusty to return
to the bar-hopping routine they had once known.

She hated to see Vern, but she had known he would be
there. The surprise was the third familiar man in the room:
C.J. Casey. Her nervous stomach rolled into an even
tighter ball, and all warmth fled her hands. Dusty introduced her to everyone, but she barely listened to the
names of the engineer and his assistant or the producer.
Her awareness was centered on the slender, bearded man
seated on one of the stools, his bootheels hooked on the
lower rung. What was Casey doing there? She had known

that she would have to face him sometime, but the first day she was set to record was the worst time she could have picked. "And you know Casey, of course," Dusty said genially, nodding toward him.

"Sure," Casey answered, extending one large, bony hand to her to shake. His palm closed around her hand, warm and dry, and Cathleen was uncomfortably aware of her ice-cold fingers and damp palms. "How are you, Cathleen?" His rich, husky voice could never be remote. When he spoke or sang half a million people felt themselves intimately alone with him. But there was a reserve, a formality in his tone which Cathleen hadn't heard there before, and it started an ache in her chest.

Cathleen wet her lips before she could speak. "I'm okay. Well, actually, not at the moment. I'm rather nervous."

"You'll do fine," he reassured her, the pale blue eyes warming. "Just remember, you're the best damn singer I've heard in a long time."

"Thank you." Cathleen hesitated, searching for a way to phrase her question that didn't sound impolite. "Did you drop by to listen to Dusty?"

"I finished recording about an hour ago, and I'm staying to do my number with Dusty. Want us to break the ice, or would you rather get it over with?"

"Oh, no, you go first. I'll listen in the control room."

"Okay."

"All right, everybody, let's get going," Dick Havermeyer, the producer, announced.

The men returned from the hall, and the musicians and singers settled onto their various chairs and stools as they pulled their instruments from the cases and tuned them. Casey raised one booted foot to a higher rung so he could prop his guitar on his leg. He bent his head to listen as he tuned it, his entire attention centered on the guitar. As she watched him, warmth trembled through Cathleen's abdomen. His long fingers caressing the strings and his complete focus on the instrument he loved stirred something deep inside her. Casey glanced up, caught her watching him and smiled, the former distance gone. A smile burst from her, radiant in its pleasure.

Cathleen followed the engineer, his assistant and the producer into the small control room, where she could listen without creating any extraneous noise. Dusty and Casey talked together in low voices, and Casey leaned back his head and bellylaughed at one of Dusty's remarks. His white teeth gleamed in contrast to his dark beard, and his pale blue eyes darkened, sparkling. Cathleen shivered. The engineer's assistant solicitously asked her if she were cold. She smiled and shook her head, turning her attention back to the studio.

She wondered what it was about Casey that gave him his enormous appeal, his blatantly sensual attraction. Each feature taken by itself was handsome, but none of them alone held the secret to his charisma. There was the voice, of course, its rasp evocative of a man in the grip of desire. And the long, slender hands with their intensely masculine tendons. The slouching walk. The compelling blue eyes. Together they added up to a man any woman would feel drawn to. But there was something more to Casey, an intangible quality—an aura of sexuality. It was part of his personality, his very being. Cathleen suspected that it originated in his deep sexual appetite. He liked women, she thought. Truly liked them, with none of the lurking fear of the female that so many men had. He enjoyed women, both in bed and out. It was obvious in the way he smiled at women and talked to them—young, old, pretty or indifferent, Casey was always at ease and interested.

Dusty and the musicians conferred briefly, glancing now and then at the sheets of music before them. They were singing the only one of Dusty's old hits to be included in the album, "Sullivan's Fall." It was the story of a high-riding rodeo star finally brought down by a woman he couldn't tame, and Casey had written it for Dusty soon after they met. The producer had wanted to avoid the pitfall of making the album merely a compilation of Dusty's former hits, but he had made an exception for this

song. It would provide a necessary tie with the past, yet
still sound fresh, since it would be sung by both Dusty and
Casey.

The men tinkered with the song before they began
recording, playing with the rhythm and adding frills or
going off in other directions. It was a method of practicing,
unique to country and western music, called "a head
session." Written music wasn't sacred in Nashville, where
so many talented musicians, particularly the early ones,
had been unable to read a note of music. So even when
there was a written score, they went through a sort of jam
session, adding to, deleting from, changing and strength-
ening the song. The product they emerged with this time
was a slightly faster version of "Sullivan's Fall," with more
drums in it than the original had had. Cathleen shook her
head, impressed, as always, by the musicians' innate
musical knowledge. The new version helped blend Casey
and Dusty's voices, which were too similar without the
sweet, higher tone of Cathleen's voice to balance their
rougher ones.

Dusty and Casey sang together with an ease that came
from many night-long sessions of talking, drinking and
"picking." They exchanged verses and swooped in together on the chorus in a seemingly effortless synchronization.
Cathleen listened and watched, so caught up in their
singing that she forgot her own nervousness. It seemed as
if very little time had passed before they were through and
the engineer was switching off the recording equipment.

A sudden lump developed in Cathleen's throat as she
realized that her time had come, but it wasn't as bad as
before. Watching them had helped soothe her nerves. She
exited the control room and hurried toward her father and
Casey, beaming. "You all were terrific!"

"Thank you, honey. You ready to do your bit?"

"Sure."

Casey rose and stretched, catching his hands above his
head and turning them inside out to ease the tension in his
mobile fingers. He released them with a yawn and began
packing his guitar in its case. "You going to sing now,

Cathleen?" he asked almost indifferently, partially turned
away from her.

"Yes. First one with Dusty and then my solo."

"The one you sang the other night?"

"No. Another one, 'Long Time.' 'Jody' is too complicat-
ed." Cathleen paused and drew in a breath. Dusty had
wandered off to speak with Jim, and this was as close to a
private conversation with Casey as she'd get here.
"I . . . uh, I'd like to talk to you later."

He turned, his eyes questioning. "Okay. I was planning
to stay to listen to you sing. Why don't I drive you home
afterward? Will Dusty be staying here?"

"Yeah, he wants to do another song this afternoon if he
can. I'd appreciate a ride home." She didn't really like the
thought of being trapped with Casey in as small an area as
a car, but it had the advantage of taking a predetermined
amount of time, after which she could leave and not see
him again. And Casey would have to keep his eyes on the
road, not on her, which would help her not to get
sidetracked.

Casey shot her a sideways glance, and she knew he was
curious about why she wanted to talk to him. She knew she
could apologize to him right there and then, but the other
people standing around inhibited her. It was too private a
matter to be overheard.

As if to emphasize how public it was, Vern strolled over
to them and slid his arm around Cathleen's shoulders.
"Hi, doll. Long time since I've seen you," he said,
grinning.

Cathleen wished she could shrug off his grasp. She
didn't like him, never had. It wasn't just that she was
afraid he would encourage her father to drink. There was a
phony ring to his "good old boy" manner and a veiled
contempt in his eyes whenever he looked at her. His touch
was repugnant to her.

Casey's glance flickered from her to Vern, his blue eyes
unreadable. She wondered what he thought of Vern. And
what did he think of Vern's hugging her? She shook the
thought from her mind. How silly—C.J. Casey wouldn't

care who touched her. Whatever interest he might have
had in her earlier was gone—she hadn't seen him in almost
a month—and it had never been deep enough to be
proprietary. As if to prove his indifference, Casey turned
away and sauntered out of the room.

She chatted with Vern for a few awkward minutes and
eased out of his grasp. Everyone else had wandered into
the hall for a short break, and she followed them. Dusty
was smoking a cigarette and chatting with the producer.
She didn't want to interrupt that, so she roamed down the
hall and found a water fountain where she could wet her
increasingly dry throat. By the time she returned, everyone was assembling once more in the studio. Cathleen
walked to the high stool beside Dusty, where Casey had
sat earlier, and climbed onto it. Her hands knotted in her
lap, and she set her feet together on the highest rung, legs
tight together.

She let Dusty lead the way in the head session, even
though the song was one of hers, "Dreamer." He and the
others knew far more than she did about arranging and
recording a song. Besides, she was too tense to enter into
it right now. She wished she had something to do with her
hands, but it was pointless for her to play an instrument
when her skill was inferior to the others' here. She shot a
glance at the glass-enclosed control room. Casey stood
watching her, arms folded across his chest. He smiled
faintly and gave her a reassuring nod, and his gesture
helped calm the tumult in her stomach.

"You ready, honey?" Dusty asked, and Cathleen nodded, wetting her lips. He began the delicate, slightly
wistful tune of "Dreamer," and Cathleen was suddenly
seized by the fear that she would freeze and be unable to
utter a sound. But when Dusty nodded, she slid into the
words just as she had the many times they had practiced it.

They sang the first verse and the chorus together, then
Dusty took the second verse and she had the third. The
final verse was sung together again. Cathleen was amazed
when she sang the chorus for the last time and realized
that the song was over. She had gotten through it without

losing her voice or forgetting a word. It hadn't been a sparkling performance. Her voice was capable of much more. But at least she had done it. She relaxed a little. The second take was a total mess, with both her and Dusty flubbing their lines several times. Finally Dusty burst into laughter, and everyone joined him, including Cathleen.

The third time they tried it, Cathleen sang into her mike, relaxed and almost comfortable now, in tune with her music. Her voice was pure as silver, wispy and floating as a cloud, matching the tune and lyrics of her song. She knew it was an excellent take, at least for her and Dusty. Since each musician and singer had a separate mike and the different tracks were combined later, on the final recording the best instrumental would be put together with the best vocal.

Cathleen was more relaxed and confident as they recorded her solo. Again Dusty took the lead in the head session, but this time Cathleen offered a few comments, too. When Dusty began the guitar intro for the first taping, she flashed him a smile and moved easily into the song, "Well, it's been a long, long time . . ."

Cathleen's voice soared, and she was sure she had done it perfectly the first time. However, they taped it three more times, trying to improve. Finally they finished the song and took a break. Cathleen wiggled off the high stool, suddenly aware of how weak and cramped her legs were. She had been so tense earlier that her muscles had knotted. Now she was shaky with an overload of adrenaline, but bursting with joy and pride. She had come through with flying colors, she knew, and the thought made her almost giddy. Laughing, grinning, chatting, she hugged Dusty enthusiastically and shook all the musicians' hands, thanking each for his skill.

Cathleen turned and saw Casey coming out of the control room, his face lit up. "Darlin', you were beautiful!"

Cathleen laughed with sheer pleasure. Casey held out his arms, and she stepped into them without thinking. His arms enclosed her, hauntingly warm and familiar. Suddenly she was no longer thinking of the song she had just taped, but luxuriating in the tingling pleasure of being held by Casey. She heard the loud thud of his heart beneath her ear, felt the rigid lines of his ribcage, smelled the warm fragrance of his skin mingled with a trace of masculine cologne. With an awful sinking feeling in the pit of her stomach, she knew that stepping into his embrace had been a huge mistake.

Chapter 6

CASEY PUT HIS HANDS ON HER SHOULDERS AND SET HER AWAY so he could look at her. His eyes were bright, their color emphasized by the tiny lines radiating from the corners and his tanned skin. Cathleen sensed that he wanted to kiss her, and she was glad there were so many people around. His hands dropped to his side. "It's a hit, honey. Watch—'Dreamer' will be the first single released from this album."

She shook her head. "Oh, no, it'll be yours and Dusty's song. You two are the names."

"You and Dusty sound ten times better than he and I do. If they're smart, 'Dreamer' will be first."

Cathleen couldn't imagine it, but she knew Casey was wiser in the ways of this business than she—or Dusty, for that matter. Dusty might have gotten Casey his start, but Cathleen was positive Casey would have become a star anyway. Besides his talent and charisma, he had an innate understanding of the music business. Cathleen stepped back, awkward under his gaze. "I . . . uh . . . I'm ready to go home if you are."

"No more back slapping?"

She smiled. "No, they need to get on with things. The session's almost up."

"Okay." He took her arm to guide her out the door, and Cathleen tried to ignore the feel of his fingers on her skin.

She waved at Dusty. "Bye. Casey's going to drive me home."

"Okay. See you there." Dusty gave her an absentminded wave, his mind on the next song.

They walked to the metal door at the far end of the hall. It opened onto the back parking lot, where most of the record company employees parked their cars. Casey led Cathleen to his beige Mercedes, chatting lightly about the recording session.

"You don't like Vern much, do you?" he asked conversationally as he opened her door.

"No, not particularly," Cathleen admitted. "What do you think of him?"

Casey shrugged as he slid under the wheel and started the engine. "He's okay, if you like snake oil salesmen."

A giggle escaped her. "What makes you say that? I don't like him because he's a boozer, and I'm afraid he'll influence Dusty the wrong way. But why do you distrust him?"

"General principles, I guess. Maybe I'm paranoid, but I used to think he encouraged Dusty in his lies and fantasies, particularly about me. Once Dusty was quizzing me about where I'd been the night before, because he was sure I'd been with Stella. It made me mad, so I refused to tell him. Old Vern threw Dusty this 'See? What'd I tell you?' look. Dusty took Vern under his wing like he did me, but Vern's career never went anywhere. He's a good guitarist and his voice is decent, but he hasn't got stage presence. I think Vern resented my success."

They were silent for a few moments while Cathleen tried to work up the courage to apologize. Apologies didn't come easily to her. She hated the emotional soul-baring which they entailed, and she dreaded the possibility that the other person might not forgive her. She wet her lips, clasping her hands firmly together. "Casey . . ."

"Yeah?" He shot her a brief sideways glance, then returned his attention to the road.

"I-I want to apologize for what I said about you and Stella."

Again he looked at her, his face conveying faint surprise. "Are you saying you believe me?"

"Yes. I believed you as soon as you said it, but I was too stunned and unhappy to tell you. I'm sorry for misjudging you. It was terribly narrowminded of me. Maybe I was looking for a scapegoat, someone I could blame instead of my parents."

He was silent for so long that Cathleen's heart sank miserably. He wasn't going to forgive her. But then he reached across the seat and wrapped one of her clenched hands in his large palm. "It's all right. I don't blame you. You were a kid, and you believed what your father told you."

"Thank you. It's not excuse enough. I continued to believe it long after I was a kid. I feel . . . awful about it. I didn't think I was that prejudiced. Everybody says I'm easygoing. But I guess I'm not very level-headed about that subject."

"It's an emotional issue. When I got my divorce, I was a little crazy myself. It's worse on kids."

"You're very understanding." She turned toward him, examining his profile.

"I wasn't for a while. It hurt to know you thought I was capable of doing that to Dusty—hurt so much it surprised me. I figured you didn't even listen to my side. So I stayed away." His thumb slid down the back of her hand and along one finger, then returned. It was a slow, rhythmic rubbing, his hard skin rasping over her smooth flesh. Casey seemed to be doing it absentmindedly, but Cathleen could think of nothing else but his touch. He grinned shamefacedly. "Staying away was damned tough, I'll tell you. I kept thinking maybe I could seduce you despite your opinion of me." He paused again. "I'm glad you believed me." He turned to look at her, and Cathleen made herself meet his eyes, her stomach quivering. "If we're friends now, how about that celebration dinner?"

Excitement fluttered in her stomach, and Cathleen knew that she very much wanted to accept him. Wanted, too, everything that would probably follow from accepting him. But she was certain that for the sake of her long-term sanity and peace of mind, she shouldn't go out with him. It was asking for trouble. She was torn with indecision, confused, never having felt so split against herself before. "Oh, no, just look at what I have on." She glanced down at her casual jeans and blouse, seizing the first excuse she happened on.

"I'll take you home to change," he countered, his brow knitting slightly in puzzlement. He jiggled her hand. "Hey, did I come on too strong the other times? Just because you go out with me doesn't mean we have to end up in bed tonight." He grinned. "Not that I have any objections to it. But I won't pressure you."

She met his faintly amused glance. "That'd be a first."

He chuckled, his expression rueful, but his eyes dancing with merriment. "Okay, okay. Maybe I got carried away before. I apologize. I hadn't planned it, either time. It just seemed to happen. But I promise I'll exercise all my control tonight. Now, how about it?"

"You must think I'm awfully naive."

"In some ways, yes. In other ways you're frighteningly mature. It makes me forget how young you are."

"What do you mean?"

He squinted one eye, thinking. "It's hard to describe. You have poise and confidence, a sort of practical 'I know what I'm doing' look to you, even when you're cutting a record for the first time."

"I grew up in the industry."

"It's more than that. You look like you can handle yourself—and others."

"Meaning I'm bossy?" She laughed. "I guess that put me in my place."

"No, meaning you act like someone with more experi-

ence of life and people than most of us have at . . . what,
twenty-five?"

"Twenty-six," she replied absently, considering his
words. "Maybe you're right. With parents like mine, I had
to learn things early. I was the one who kept our lives
running on time and on the right track. Neither Dusty nor
Stella was very practical or reliable."

"That's an understatement."

"So it was up to me and Lynette. I was better at
ordinary things than she was. She's not as bad as Stella or
Dusty, but . . ."

"I get your drift. You had an abnormal childhood."

"Did I? It was the only one I knew."

"Most kids don't screen their parents' calls or remind
them of their appointments or tell the servants what to do,
all of which I remember you doing. They don't keep
musicians' hours or rub shoulders with famous people."
Or take care of an alcoholic and witness the wild emotional outbursts both Cathleen's parents were famous for,
Casey added mentally. He felt a faint, sad ache for her
childhood and adolescence. He squeezed her hand. "But
not so much experience with dating or men?"

She shook her head. "Not men like you." Cathleen bit
her lip, wondering how much she had given away with that
statement. "I mean . . ."

"Yes?" One brow lifted teasingly. "I'm intrigued."

"Oh, you know. Sophisticated."

"Sophisticated!" He burst into genuine laughter and
cast an amused eye down at his simple, faded jeans and
dark green T-shirt. "This is sophisticated?"

"I don't mean clothes," she retorted irritably. "Or
talking like somebody from Boston. You've been so many
places and seen so much. You have experience and charm.
Don't grin at me like that. You know you do!"

"I'll bow to your superior judgment."

"Casey, don't be difficult. You've been with a lot of
women far more sophisticated than I am—you're bound to
expect more from me than I know how to give."

"This isn't a job application. I like you the way you are.

Even when you're prickly and angry with me. Look, Cathleen, I promise I won't push. At least not tonight. Okay?"

Cathleen bit her lip, torn by indecision. "I've tried never to get involved with anyone in country and western music," she murmured hesitantly.

"Make an exception."

She sighed. "Oh, Casey, you're more than an exception. You shatter the whole rule. You're exactly what I've tried to avoid."

"Why put restrictions on your life? Why not go out with whomever you want and have a good time and to hell with whether they're singers or doctors or mechanics? Why all the fences, Cathleen?"

She set her jaw. When he put it that way, she felt silly and narrow and wrong. "Surely you must realize. I don't want to be like my parents."

"Marrying—which is *not* what we were talking about— someone outside the music industry doesn't guarantee that you won't get divorced."

"I know. But it has to give you a better chance," Cathleen insisted stubbornly.

Casey sighed as he turned the elegant Mercedes onto Cathleen's street. "Sometimes, Cath, you could drive a man to brutality. When you said you believed me, I thought we'd passed the hurdle, but you keep coming up with objections. Lady, I think you're flat-out scared of getting into a situation where you don't have control."

Her stomach did a curious flip-flop. "What does that mean?"

"It means you're terrified of being loose and emotional, or following your instincts. In short, you're scared you'll turn out like your parents. Who knows what might happen if you let go, or weren't in command of a situation? You might lose your sense and become ruled by something else—your emotions, or alcohol."

Casey pulled into the driveway of her house and stopped the car. Cathleen stared at him, unable to speak. He turned and settled his arm along the back of the seat.

Cathleen glanced away, then swallowed and wet her lips. Was he right? His words had hit her right in the gut, leaving her breathless and stunned. She looked back at him, eyes rounded and a little frightened, and his expression softened. He stretched out a hand and slid it over her dark, silken hair.

"I'm sorry," he said softly. "I had no right to say that. I was frustrated and popping off."

"Maybe you're right. I don't like to be helpless or not in control of myself. And that's the way I feel around you." Her shy, upward glance at him through her lashes sent a hot stab through his abdomen.

Casey sucked in his breath. "Take a chance. Please? I won't seduce you. Okay?"

Cathleen hesitated. "Okay." She smiled brilliantly. Something dark and wild flashed in the depths of Casey's eyes and was gone before she could be sure she had witnessed it. They left the car and walked up the side steps to the kitchen door. "Hope you don't mind coming in the back way."

"I feel more comfortable slipping in the back door," he joked. "I haven't gone in my front door but about three times since I moved there."

Cathleen smiled. Her former reservations about Casey were slipping away at an alarming rate. She unlocked the kitchen door and went inside, Casey on her heels. "Would you like a drink? I have soft drinks, or I could make coffee. Sorry, but we don't keep any beer in the fridge."

He shook his head. "I don't need beer. Anything's fine. A soft drink, whatever."

Cathleen took out two glasses, filled them with ice and poured in some cola, aware of his gaze following her movements. She was surprised to see Casey pull out one of the kitchen chairs and sit down, casually propping one foot on the rung of the chair beside him. It was part of his easy, casual attitude, like his homing instinct for the least formal room of any house. Cathleen sat down across from him and crossed her arms on the table before her.

"That session today was a beauty," Casey commented, smoothing his mustache with a thumb and forefinger. "I was impressed."

"Honestly?"

"Honestly. I told you, I don't lie about music."

Cathleen grinned. "I was so afraid I thought I wouldn't remember the words to the song."

"They were right in front of you."

"I know, but I'm not sure I could have read them in the state I was in."

"You looked perfectly poised."

"I must be more of an actress than I thought, then. My stomach was jumping all over the place."

"The first time I recorded at Sunburst, my knees shook. I mean literally. Thank God I had that stool." He paused. "Aside from being terrified, how'd you like it?"

Cathleen tilted her head to the side, considering. "Actually, it was fun once I got used to it. It was exciting, in spite of being frightening. I enjoy singing, and making a record was more fun than singing by myself. All the other people around helping made it better."

"Wait'll you have an audience."

"No, that would be too much. Good heavens, scared as I was to record, I'd probably have a heart attack at facing an audience."

"You'll have to, sooner or later."

"I know. Eddy's booking us a tour. I have to go for Dusty's sake, but I dread it. I don't know what to do. What if I make a fool of myself? The only time I've been on stage was when I was three and Dusty hauled Lynette and me out there with him."

"Don't worry. You're a natural. Just smile at them. Did anybody ever tell you that your smile could revive a dead man?"

"What?" She laughed. "No."

"Well, it could. It nearly knocked me out of my chair that day in the Sunburst lounge."

"Casey, come on . . ."

"I'm serious. Turn on that smile full voltage and you'll have the audience eating out of your hand. Word of honor." His eyes linked with hers, warm and inviting. "I'm beginning to regret my promise not to seduce you tonight."

"Casey . . ." she began sternly, although his words turned her soft as butter inside.

"I know, I know. I promised. Tell me something to take my mind off you."

Cathleen pushed back her chair and stood up. "I think it's time I dressed for dinner." She glanced at her watch. "Oh, it's only four-thirty. That's a little early, isn't it?"

"I have to go home to change anyway." He indicated his worn, extremely casual clothes. "Dressed like this, the only place I could take you would be a hamburger joint. Why don't I return to pick you up in, say, a couple of hours?" He unfolded his long frame from the chair and ambled to the door, turning to smile and wink at her. "See you at about six-thirty."

After he left Cathleen floated to her bedroom. The good taping session that afternoon, combined with the prospect of spending the evening with Casey, buoyed her spirits to the point of effervescence. She had the distinct suspicion that she was getting in over her head, but at the moment she couldn't have cared less. The feeling was too enjoyable to ruin with doubts.

She ran a tub of water, liberally laced it with bubble bath, and took a nice, long soak. Idly her mind roamed over the afternoon's events, recalling her fear before the session and her rush of exultation when she finished the song, remembering Casey as he watched her and later as they talked in his car. She went over every nuance, every tone, every detail of his looks and clothes, hardly noticing the water cooling around her. Finally she shivered, bringing herself back to the present, and stepped out to towel herself dry. Then, kneeling beside the tub, she shampooed her hair.

Afterward she dressed and dried her hair. She stared at

her reflection in the mirror for a moment, wishing there were some way she could make her hair look more elegant. At chin length, it was too short to put up satisfactorily. She brushed one side back and fastened it with a decorative barrette, leaving the other side swinging free. It added a certain flair and vivacity, she decided, pleased with her efforts. She applied her makeup with extra care, subtly deepening the color of her eyes and emphasizing their beauty with eye shadow and mascara. After a final spray of perfume at the hollow of her throat and on her wrists, she tackled the problem of her wardrobe.

It didn't take long to select her dress, because there was one which simply cried out to be worn. It was a swirling, many-pleated crepe confection which fell straight from a horizontal neckline held up by spaghetti straps. Over it she wore a collarless, lapel-less coat of the same thin crepe. The style of the coat and dress was perfectly plain, but the material made up for it. It was a light apricot color patterned with huge splashes of white flowers and green stems. The dress caught the eye without detracting from the wearer, and the color added a soft glow to Cathleen's creamy skin. Though the soft material clung to her breasts more than she liked, the dress's straight lines at least didn't emphasize her curvaceous figure, as many evening dresses did.

Cathleen stepped into high-heeled white sandals and fastened the cross-straps before taking a final twirl in front of the full-length mirror. Exhilarated by the attractive image she presented, Cathleen hummed to herself as she removed a small white leather handbag from a drawer. She transferred the essentials from her everyday purse into the smaller bag and strode into the living room to wait for Casey. There she slid onto the piano bench and, after limbering up her fingers, tackled a classical piano sonata she had learned long ago. Her memory was fragmentary, and she stumbled over many of the notes, but the difficult music took her mind off waiting, and the steadily building path to the climax of the piece suited her mood. Something loud and fast, that was what she wanted—something her fingers could fly over.

"Good Lord, what's got into you, girl?"

Cathleen whirled around to see her father. He grinned, arms crossed over his chest.

Cathleen giggled nervously. "I'm waiting for Casey, and I decided to play a little. It'll help get rid of that extra adrenaline I worked up at the studio."

"Casey, huh?" His smile widened. "So he *is* taken with you. I'm surprised he hasn't been here more often."

"Daddy! You're as bad as Lynette for finding romance in the simplest friendships."

"The way you're dressed doesn't look like friendship, girl."

Cathleen shrugged. "There isn't going to be anything else."

"C.J. Casey's mighty persuasive." Dusty's eyes twinkled.

"Daddy," Cathleen fixed him with a stern gaze, "fathers aren't supposed to be delighted at the prospect of their daughters' seduction."

"Is *that* what's going to happen tonight?" he teased.

"No! Definitely not. But you're supposed to be afraid it will. You should go stiff and Victorian and say something like, 'Watch out for Casey, baby. I know his kind, 'cause I was just like him. He's interested in only one thing.'"

Dusty laughed. "What's that?"

Cathleen threw him a dirty look. "I give up. You're incorrigible." She smiled at him fondly, then stood up and linked one of her arms through his. "Casey and I are going out to celebrate getting through my first recording session without me making an utter fool of myself."

"You did better than that, Cathy. You were sensational."

"Flattery will get you everywhere. Speaking of things like love lives and evenings out, what are you doing tonight?"

"Nothing exciting. Jim and Vern are coming over, and we'll do a little picking."

Cathleen quickly suppressed her flicker of unease. "What, no lady friend? Dusty, have you lost your touch?"

"I hope not. But I'm not driven, like I used to be. I don't need a new girl every night to prove I don't care about Stella. I'll wait till I find somebody special."

His daughter gave his arm a little squeeze, filled with pride at another indication of Dusty's hard-won knowledge and maturity. "Good luck. I hope she happens by real soon."

He shrugged. "I can wait. Patience is a virtue, so they tell me."

"That's what I've heard."

"I'm content just as I am. Suppose that means I'm getting old?"

"No, just that you're getting your head on straight."

"About time, I guess, since I'm almost sixty."

They strolled through the hall into the den as they talked. Cathleen stopped and hugged her father. "Oh, Dusty, I love you."

"I love you, too, sweetheart." The doorbell rang, and Dusty eased out of her embrace. "That must be Casey. Better answer the door."

Cathleen smiled, swallowing the teary ache in her throat, and walked across the hall to open the front door. As her father had predicted, Casey stood on the doorstep. Cathleen's eyes widened appreciatively when she saw him. In honor of the occasion he had changed into a creamy off-white suit, obviously tailor-made to fit him by the way it followed the lines of his body. Although he had not gone so far as to wear a tie—she had once heard Casey remark that he didn't own a single tie—he wore a rich silk shirt of a deep wine color beneath the suit jacket. He was half turned away when she opened the door, gazing across their front lawn and whistling beneath his breath, and he turned to face her, his face subtly changing to reflect a look of stunned admiration. "Cathleen—you look beautiful."

His words and look sizzled through her, and she was suddenly breathless. "Thank you." She strove to put some flippancy into her voice. "So do you."

He didn't step inside, but continued to look at her, his eyes sliding leisurely over her, missing nothing. Cathleen shifted and he glanced back up at her face, a faint smile tracing his lips. "Make you nervous?"

"A little."

He took her hand, and Cathleen hurriedly called back a good-bye in Dusty's direction as Casey pulled her out the door. "Let me tell you something," Casey said as they strolled to the car. "That wasn't sophistication you saw in me a minute ago. It was pure, dumbstruck awe."

"You're teasing me."

"Only a bit. You're gorgeous." His hand left hers and slid around her waist. He bent until his mouth grazed her ear. "Now, if you'd only learn to show off that nice body of yours a little more . . ."

Cathleen pushed ineffectually at his hand, which now rested intimately on her hipbone. "Casey, you promised."

His lips lightly brushed her temple. "I promised not to push you into anything. I didn't say I wouldn't flirt."

She chuckled. "I should have known you'd have an excuse."

Casey handed her into the car and slid into the other side. The Mercedes started with a low-pitched purr, and he backed out of the driveway. Cathleen relaxed in her plush leather seat and leaned her head against the headrest. Casey pushed a cassette into the tape deck, and immediately music welled around them, the excellent tape system enclosing them with the rich throb of guitars, fiddles and drums. The artist was a male country and western singer whom Cathleen particularly liked, and she gave herself up gladly to the music. Casey glanced at her and smiled. He wondered if she had any idea how she intrigued and enticed him. Her body stirred him physically, and her often caustic wit amused him. Even her flashes of anger and the glimpses of her innocence lured him. But the almost frightening thing was the effect of her smile and her silver-clear voice; when she sang or when she smiled at him, she reached out and laid claim to his soul.

Chapter 7

THEY DINED AT AN EXCLUSIVE RESTAURANT LOCATED IN A refurbished old mansion. To Cathleen's surprise, Casey led her around to the side door of the establishment. They opened the door and stepped into a foyer that was richly decorated with thick red carpet and oak paneling. Narrow polished stairs rose to the right, and in front of them lay a hall. Casey stopped beside the staircase, and Cathleen glanced up at him questioningly. "What are we doing?" she whispered.

"Why are you whispering?" he countered teasingly, his rich voice loud in the elegant chamber.

"I don't know. It seems appropriate." She swept one hand around to indicate the room.

"What we're doing, darlin', is paying the price of fame."

"Oh." She understood what he meant. They were entering unobtrusively in an attempt to escape the stares, whispered comments and importunate demands of other diners. The sheer expensiveness of a restaurant didn't necessarily eliminate such problems; wealthy fans could be as pressing and inconsiderate as any others.

Within moments a waiter appeared. Starched, graying and immaculate, he could easily have passed for a high-level diplomat. He inclined his head regally and allowed them a thin, frosty smile. "Mr. Casey. Ma'am. I hope I haven't kept you waiting long."

"No. It's fine."

"Excellent. If you will follow me, please, I have your table set up." To Cathleen's surprise he started up the stairs. Casey moved to follow, his hand under Cathleen's elbow, and after a moment's startled hesitation she went along. At the top of the stairs they entered a short hall, which they crossed to the longer hall beyond. Through an open door Cathleen glimpsed a richly decorated room containing a marble fireplace and two round tables for four, one of them occupied. The waiter whisked them past the door and into another room. Smaller than the one she had seen earlier, this chamber contained no fireplace and only one table. However, it lacked nothing in elegance. Here, too, oak paneling ran a few feet up the wall, topped by wainscoting, and above that lay pale blue wallpaper with the watery look of moiré silk.

Their waiter solemnly held out a chair to seat her and presented oversized menus with a flourish. "I will be serving you tonight," he announced as if bestowing a great honor. "Would you care for something from the bar?"

Casey looked inquiringly at Cathleen, and she hesitated. She drank so rarely that she was always at a loss as to what to order. "They make a good gin fizz here," Casey suggested. "It's New Orleans style."

"Okay, I'll trust your judgment."

"Ramos gin fizz," Casey told the waiter.

"Very good. And a Manhattan for you, sir?"

"Fine."

After the waiter left Cathleen leaned forward, her eyes sparkling with amusement. "Very impressive."

"Oh, Raymond's famous for putting on a show. The memory's part of his quintessential maître d' image."

"And here I thought he remembered because you ordered it so often," she teased.

"Now, now."

They opened the wide menus to study them, casually discussing the choice of foods. The restaurant specialized in elegant dishes, and Cathleen mentally consigned her unending diet to perdition as she selected a veal dish with béarnaise sauce.

"Do you like shrimp?" Casey asked.

"Love it."

"Good. Let's have shrimp cocktails. They fly the shrimp in from the coast."

Raymond appeared silently, and Cathleen wondered how he had perfected the art of walking without making any noise. He carried a small silver tray which held their drinks, and, like a surgeon performing a delicate operation, he laid cocktail napkins beside their water goblets, then set the glasses down on them. "I trust everything is satisfactory?"

"Of course." It was obviously the answer Raymond expected. Casey ordered their meals, ending with a request for an hors d'oeuvre tray. "They have the best appetizers," he explained to Cathleen as Raymond left the room. "Fried zucchini, mushrooms, potato peels—weird things, but delicious. The chef makes tiny hamburgers with cherry tomatoes and a cocktail onion and funny little buns."

"Casey, you're a child at heart."

"Of course," he replied easily. "That's why I like being a singer. All I do is play, even when I'm working."

"You are also wreaking havoc with my diet," she admonished.

"Your diet? Women!" He shook his head. "Why do they always think they have to be on a diet?"

"Because I'm short and stocky."

Casey made a rude noise of disbelief. "I like your body the way it is. Believe me, your weight's in exactly the right places." He stretched one arm across the table to lay his hand on hers. "Didn't I tell you how beautiful you look tonight?"

"I'm not sure. You can tell me again."

"Well, honey, you're gorgeous. In fact, you make it damn hard to remember my promise."

"Casey . . ." she began warningly.

"Don't worry. I won't break it. Fortunately, I have tremendous self-control." He grinned.

"Uh-huh." Cathleen's voice conveyed supreme disbelief.

He watched her, his eyes darkening slightly as he caressed the back of her hand with the faintest brush of his fingertips. Cathleen's throat tightened. Unexpectedly he pulled his hand back. "We better get off the subject, or I may prove myself a liar."

"Okay. What would you like to talk about?"

"Anything. When are you going on tour?"

"They're rushing the album out, so we'll start a week after the banquet for Dusty."

"That reminds me. Dick Eberhardt called me today. He's in charge of the show for the banquet."

"They're having a floor show?"

"Nothing big, just a tribute to Dusty. There'll be an emcee talking about Dusty's life, and several people are going to give testimonials."

"It doesn't sound like something Dusty will like."

"Probably a dead bore," he agreed.

"And embarrassing. Dusty will hate having all those nice things said about him."

"Maybe he'll like the singing better. Dick plans to have me and two or three others sing Dusty's songs. He wants you and me to sing a couple of songs that Dusty and Stella used to sing." He paused, his eyebrows quirked, waiting for her reaction.

Cathleen hesitated. The one time she had sung with Casey, it had had a tremendous impact on her. She wasn't sure she could handle singing with him in front of a large group. "I . . . I don't know. I don't like performing."

"You'll have to do it on tour. This ought to be easier, since the audience will be smaller. A lot of them will be people you've known most of your life. It'll introduce you to live performances."

"It probably would be good practice for the tour," Cathleen conceded. She hated to reveal the real reason for her reluctance—a fear of exposing her attraction to Casey in front of hundreds of people who knew them both. It was silly. When couples sang to each other, they were supposed to look involved. Everyone would think she was acting, except Casey—but he was the person she least wanted to know.

"Come on. You'll enjoy it. Dick wants us. Apparently Metcalf told him we sounded good together. We did, you know."

"I know." She hesitated. "Well, I guess it's okay. I can do it."

"Your enthusiasm overwhelms me. You know something, Cathleen? I can't figure you out. Why are you so set against singing? You're obviously dreading the tour. You don't even want to sing at this banquet. You did your best to squirm out of the recording contract. Why?"

"Simple." She shrugged. "I don't want to be in the business. It's not for me."

"Why? I can't imagine a kid of Dusty and Stella's not loving the spotlight."

"It's precisely because I *am* their daughter! I know what success is like. I've seen what it can do to a marriage, a family, a life. It isn't worth it to me, Casey. I'd rather be poor and anonymous."

"Not everyone in the business turns out to be like Dusty."

"Maybe not. But how many of them turn out happy? The money and acclaim don't make up for the private misery. You're hardly ever at home. There's no room in your life for a family. Day after day you're on buses and airplanes, and night after night you're singing in front of a bunch of people you don't know. The public turns on you if you do anything wrong. You're constantly on display. Reporters spy on you; people gawk at you in the street. It's not worth it. I love singing. But I don't have the personality for success. So I plan to stick to writing songs."

"You're presuming that this album and tour will make you a success, which may not happen. Secondly, you assume you'd have to live the crazy life your parents did. It *can* be done differently. I spend one month a year in Las Vegas and six weeks a year on tour. The rest of the time I'm at home."

"Yeah, but you're already on top. It could kill me getting there."

"With a voice like yours, it's a crime not to sing."

"I sing now. I don't need an audience in order to enjoy it. I'm happy writing songs and singing for my own enjoyment."

He shook his head in bemusement. "I can't understand it. I'm too much of a performer. But, look, you can make this album and tour without wrecking your life. Nobody can force you to sing with Sunburst again. You can call it quits any time you want."

Cathleen sighed. "I know. What I'm afraid of is getting hooked on it. What if I *am* like Stella and Dusty and can't live without the applause? This afternoon, when I cut that record, I liked it! It was exciting. What if I enjoy it too much to quit after one album?" She stopped, surprised at having blurted that out to Casey. She would have thought he was the last person to whom she would reveal personal weakness or fear. She had told him something she wouldn't have told Eddy or Jack, or even her sister. It was crazy. She glanced at Casey to see his reaction to her confidences. He was studying her, his expression frowning and thoughtful.

"I can't tell you it wouldn't happen," he said slowly. "I'd like to, but the music business can be addictive. Wouldn't you rather know it than be afraid the rest of your life? If you discover you like the life, it's not such a problem. It isn't all terrible, honey. What you saw was the bad end—the fights, Dusty's drinking, his losing money. There's a lot of fun and joy to it, too, things you didn't see. There's the thrill of an audience loving what you did, the satisfaction of cutting an excellent song, of having money enough to live nicely and do what you want. Loosen up, Cath. Don't turn your back on it because of fear. Give it a chance. Don't hold back."

"That sounds like your philosophy."

He shrugged. "I believe in taking risks. Is that wrong?"

"For me it is." Cathleen gazed at her water goblet, running a forefinger around the rim. Casey was too reasonable. It made her sound scared and foolishly conservative.

"Cathleen, you're ten times more stable than Dusty or Stella. You don't have to worry about becoming an emotional idiot."

"Are you saying Dusty's an emotional idiot?" Cathleen flared.

"Come on, girl, we both know Dusty's got more twists to his emotions than a corkscrew. Don't try to lead me off the subject. We're discussing you, not Dusty."

"You are the pushiest person I know. Why do you presume you have the right to discuss either of us?"

"Because I care about you," he replied simply, leaving her speechless. "Hey, I'm sorry," Casey murmured and grazed her cheek with one rough fingertip. "I'm being too serious for a night on the town. I didn't mean to upset or embarrass you. We'll change the subject. Okay?"

"Okay." Cathleen glanced at him. The concern in his blue eyes was compelling, drawing her under his spell. She had the faintly sick feeling of losing control.

"Do you have your costumes for the tour yet?"

"No." Cathleen followed his change of subject thankfully. "I don't know where to go."

"Do you know Chase's designs?"

Cathleen shook her head.

"Liz Chase is fairly new around here, but she's becoming popular. I think her clothes might suit you."

Cathleen gave him a suspicious glance. "She doesn't design your costumes, does she?"

Casey laughed. "Are you hinting that my stage wardrobe leaves something to be desired?"

"Let's just say I had something in mind besides jeans and a T-shirt."

"Set your mind at rest. She doesn't design my clothes. In fact, she goes into despair everytime she sees me. You'd like her work. Want to meet her?"

"Yes, I guess so."

"Good. Why don't I take you over to her place tomorrow?"

Cathleen hesitated, buying time by selecting an appetizer from the tray Raymond had brought in while they talked. Casey was maneuvering her into seeing him again. It wouldn't be wise, yet . . . she found herself facing the risk with eagerness. Cathleen took a deep breath. "All right."

"See? That wasn't so bad, was it? Who knows? You might get to where you can tolerate my company."

"It's not that I don't like you. Surely you must know that."

"No, frankly, I don't. Even after I cleared up the mistake about me and Stella, you've been reluctant to be around me. I feel as if I'm forcing you every step of the way."

"That must be an unusual experience for you."

He shrugged. "Maybe. What I want to know is, why? At times I'd swear you're enjoying yourself."

"I am. You're funny, charming and good-looking to a point that's downright unfair. I'd be crazy not to enjoy myself."

"Then what's the problem?"

"It's against my better judgment. You're way beyond my depth."

"I won't hurt you. I'm keeping my promise, aren't I? No heavy breathing, no groping."

Cathleen had to smile. "Casey, you're hopeless. Aren't you ever serious?"

"I like to keep things in perspective with a little humor."

"No, you think I'm funny," she retorted. "I told you, I'm naive and silly compared to you." She shook her head.

"Sometimes I feel torn, as if I'm two people. I want one thing—and yet I also want something diametrically opposed to it."

"Safety and security on one hand, freedom and fun on the other?"

Cathleen glanced at him, surprised. "How did you know?"

"It doesn't take much to figure it out. You're lush and sensual, yet you try to hide it. You love singing, but refuse to do it. You'd like to make love with me, but you're scared to admit it."

"I never said that!"

"You didn't have to. I kissed you the other night, remember?"

Cathleen blushed and glanced away. Her response to his kisses had been unmistakable. Casey lifted her hand to his lips and lightly kissed it. His lips were warm, velvety, and the beard around his mouth prickled her skin. She shivered at the multitude of sensations he aroused in her.

"Don't be scared of me, Cath. I won't press you, remember?"

Cathleen's fingers tightened in his. How could she tell him she didn't fear his actions, but her own? He didn't have to press her. Merely being around him was dangerous. "I know, Casey."

"Good." He kissed her fingertips again. The door opened, and Raymond glided in. Cathleen jumped self-consciously, but Casey hardly moved except to flick a glance at the door. She pulled her hand from his grasp. For an instant Casey held on, then released her, grinning. Raymond whisked away the tray and set their shrimp cocktails before them. His face betrayed not the slightest curiosity.

Cathleen turned her attention to the shrimp. "Mmm, delicious. You were right."

Casey followed her unsubtle change of topic, and the rest of the evening was spent in light, frivolous banter. The meal was delicious. Casey persuaded her to eat one of the flaming desserts which were a specialty of the restaurant.

They talked about music and people they both knew, joked and laughed, all with the ease of old friends. But underlying everything was a strange, surging excitement whenever Casey's gaze settled on her face, or his hand grazed hers or he shifted in his chair. He appealed to her in ways too numerous to comprehend, tugging at her senses while he touched her mind and heart. The sound of his rasping voice and sudden, delighted laughter at one of her remarks . . . the sight of his downturned smile, or his eyebrow shifting upwards . . . the spicy odor of masculine cologne mingling with the warm scent of his flesh . . . Cathleen's heartbeat quickened, and her face flushed with a warmth not caused by the wine.

Disappointment mingled with relief when the meal was over. They walked outside, Cathleen intensely aware of Casey's looming presence beside her. He made no move toward her except to hold her hand lightly. Her senses were unusually acute tonight, not only to Casey but to the slight spring breeze which cooled her cheek and ruffled her hair, the crunch of gravel beneath their feet and the sweet odor of the honeysuckle that overgrew a nearby fence. The stars and quarter moon were unaccountably bright. Casey apparently felt whatever she did, because when they reached his car he pulled her against him, crossing his arms around her from behind and resting his chin on the top of her head. "Beautiful, isn't it?" he murmured. They stood for a moment in languid admiration of the night.

He rubbed his cheek against her head. "Things ought to be easy for us. Doesn't everything seem natural on a night like this?"

Unexpected tears sparkled in her eyes. She wished achingly for something she didn't know. For an instant she thought of turning in Casey's arms and burrowing against his chest. The thought frightened her, and she pulled away. Casey said nothing, although Cathleen thought she heard a tiny sigh escape his lips. He opened his arms, letting her go.

They returned to Cathleen's house silently. Cathleen knew there was no place for her to go except home. At any of the popular nightspots Casey would be instantly recognized and so besieged by fans that they wouldn't be left alone for a moment. Like most popular country and western singers, he spent most of his free time at home or at the houses of friends.

Dusty was home when they arrived, and he greeted them jovially. Casey shrugged out of his expensive jacket, rolled up the sleeves of his silk shirt and sat down cross-legged on the floor to talk to Dusty, as much at ease as he had been in the elegant restaurant. Cathleen, curiously disappointed by her father's presence, sat beside Dusty and listened to them reminisce. Casey included her in the conversation now and then with a look or a question, but most of the time she was a silent observer. After her initial irritation Cathleen enjoyed listening to them. Dusty was a veteran in the country and western business and had known performers who were legends even to Casey. He recalled bits of gossip and funny stories about the famous and less-than-famous. Casey joined in with more recent observations, his familiar husky laugh punctuating his comments. Cathleen wondered how it was possible to feel so at ease and comfortable with a man whose mere glance sent sizzles of excitement through her at other times.

A couple of hours later Casey unfolded his long frame from its cross-legged position on the floor. "About time for me to go," he commented, extending his hand to Dusty. Dusty shook it, although he offered several protestations that it was far too early to leave. Casey chuckled. "*You* may not be getting older, Dusty, but *I* am. I can't take the nightlife anymore."

"You call this nightlife?" Dusty quizzed him, the lines in his leathery face deepening with humor. "Son, you *are* getting old."

Cathleen strolled with Casey to the front door. He opened it halfway, then turned toward her. His gaze slid up her body to her face and fastened on her mouth. Cathleen swallowed. "Thank you for the dinner. It was wonderful."

"Good. I enjoyed it, too. Remember, we're going to Chase's tomorrow." Cathleen nodded. He put one hand lightly on her shoulder, then bent to brush his mouth against hers. His lips were warm and faintly moist, velvety soft. It was the briefest of caresses, a gesture made sensual only by his innate sexuality and her intense excitement. She had been on edge all evening, waiting for this kiss, and the result was like sparks to dry tinder, explosive far beyond its apparent passion. Involuntarily her hands went up to encircle his neck, but stopped in midair as Casey stepped back. Cathleen realized, bemused, that there would be nothing more. What she had thought was a prelude was beginning, middle and end. The fact that she had gone out with him only because he had promised not to seduce her didn't relieve the ache flowering in her abdomen. It was a lowering thought to realize that she wished he hadn't kept his word.

"Bye, now." He winked at her—oh, that devastating wink!—and was gone. Mechanically Cathleen closed the door, hardly aware of what she was doing. She glided down the hall to her bedroom instead of returning to the den. She didn't want Dusty's conversation right now—nor his interested speculation. All she wanted was to go to bed and sleep. She needed to block out the anticipation burgeoning in her chest at the thought of seeing Casey again tomorrow. Her life was rocketing off in crazy directions, out of control. The really frightening thing was that she didn't even care.

Casey pulled up to the house the next morning shortly before eleven. Cathleen, who had had trouble going to sleep, had risen late and was sitting in the kitchen eating her meager breakfast of toast, juice and coffee. When she saw Casey's elegant car turn into the driveway she jumped to her feet in panic, her hands flying to her hair, which lay in the fat little ringlets left by electric curlers. She bolted to her bedroom, unfastening her robe as she ran. Inside her room she dropped the robe onto the floor and whipped out the fresh red-and-white sundress she had chosen earlier.

She zipped it up the back and tied the halter strings behind her neck with trembling fingers. Why was Casey here so early? Although he hadn't set a specific time, she had expected him later in the day. Casey didn't seem the type to go anywhere in the morning. She heard his loud knock on the kitchen door as she grabbed a hairbrush and pulled it ruthlessly through her curls.

"Cathleen?" Casey's questioning voice was startlingly close. He must have opened the back door and stepped into the kitchen.

"Yes? I'll be out in a second," she called back, hoping her voice didn't shake. Casey had the ability to throw her, no matter how simple the situation. She heard his heels on the vinyl floor of the kitchen, then in the hallway. Cathleen whirled as he reached her door. "Oh! I—why didn't you stay in the kitchen?"

He grinned. "Probably hoping I'd catch you dressing."

"Casey!"

"Surprised? I thought you had me pegged as a lecher."

"Would you please leave? I haven't finished getting ready," she went on crossly. "What are you doing here so early?"

"Couldn't wait to see you. What's the matter? You look lovely."

"I don't have on any makeup, and my hair's not combed."

"I like you the way you are." His eyes darkened, and a low rasp threaded his voice. "Barefoot, your hair mussed. You look as if you're on your way to bed."

His words set her heart to knocking violently, and her breath surged in her throat. She wet her suddenly dry lips, then realized it had been the wrong gesture to make, for his heavy-lidded eyes widened and he moved toward her in strides far more rapid than his usual lazy walk. Cathleen stared, unmoving, as he stopped before her and slid his hands into her hair with excruciating slowness. She could feel the tips of his fingers gliding over the thin skin of her scalp, feel her individual hairs parting before his fingers and softly curving around them.

"Your hair is like silk." The rich timbre of his voice took all triteness from the words, making them a new and intimate statement that shook her with its intensity. "Except it's far thicker. You tempt me, Cathleen Richards. You really tempt me. I never dreamed—after all these years—I'd have so much trouble keeping my hands off a woman."

She could feel the infinitesimal tremor of his fingers against her scalp, and it affected her more than any impassioned avowal could have. He wanted her. His fingers transmitted the desperate ache to her flesh. It was hot and elemental and almost unbearably provocative. Cathleen yearned for his touch, his kiss. His eyes were dark as night, the lids drooping sensually, and the tight lines around his mouth and eyes slackened with sexual hunger. He pulled her closer as his fingers rubbed her scalp hypnotically. Cathleen obeyed his touch without thought, moving so near his body that she could feel the heat of his skin through their clothes. Her flesh prickled at his proximity, anticipating the feel of his body upon hers.

Casey lowered his head, eyes closing in a manner expressive of surrender, and his lips sought hers. Cathleen never thought of pulling away. Instead she lifted her face to meet him, memorizing the flashing glance of Casey's face, soft and vulnerable in its hunger, the fragile eyelids weighed down by thick, smoky lashes. Their mouths met, clung, melted into one another. Cathleen went up on tiptoes to press her body into him, and his arms surrounded her, hard and urgent. She heard the harsh intake of his breath, felt the prickle of his mustache and beard upon her skin, breathed in the clean, faintly soapy scent of his skin. Her arms slid around his neck and pulled her to him more tightly.

His tongue was delighting her mouth, stroking the sensitive flesh of her inner cheeks, rubbing her tongue and curling agilely around it. She responded with innocent relish, thrusting her tongue into his mouth in imitation of his movements. His mouth widened as if to consume her, and his lips dug deeper into hers. Casey crushed her to

him, arms digging into her back and stamping the iron heat
of his need into her pliant flesh.

He lifted her, sliding his mouth down her neck, savoring
the exquisitely tender skin of her throat. His tongue
dipped into the fragile hollow created by her collarbone,
and a faint, breathy moan came from Cathleen's mouth.
Her head lolled back, as if to give him freer access to her
throat. Casey's breath came hard and fast, and his hands
seared her where they touched. One hand glided down
over her dress to the hem and came up under the skirt,
caressing the bare skin of her leg. His fingers were spread,
touching every inch of skin he could as his hand moved
slowly upward in ever higher circles until finally his
fingertips brushed the lace trim of her panties.

He teased at the edging before moving on to the flimsy
cloth covering her buttocks. Before long his fingers returned to the lace trim, tracing it, then insinuating themselves beneath the edge. Cathleen drew in her breath
sharply at the intimate touch and stirred in his arms, with
the result that even more skin was exposed to his searching
fingers. He groaned softly and let her slide down his body,
her soft flesh dragging over his hard bone and muscle.
Questioningly she looked up at him. Casey's face was
dark, suffused with passion, and his eyes glittered wildly.
He was a man on the edge, she realized, very close to
losing control. Casey swallowed and moved back. His gaze
fell to her breasts, falling and rising with her rapid
breathing. Her nipples pressed against the cloth of the
dress in a clear and unmistakable message. He cupped her
breasts with his hands, studying them as his thumbs
brushed the engorged peaks.

His voice was shaky. "I want to see your breasts, to hold
them, naked. Touch your nipples with my fingers . . . with
my tongue." A shiver ran through Cathleen, and her
knees almost buckled. A white-hot flame speared her.
"But if I go on now, I can't stop. You understand?"
Cathleen nodded mutely. He sighed and leaned his forehead against the top of her head. "It's an awkward time
and place. I promised I'd move slowly. I don't want to

rush. It should be nice and slow, no worrying whether Dusty might come in." He kissed her hair and moved reluctantly away. "I'll wait for you in the den." His voice was hoarse and taut with effort, and he looked past her instead of into her face.

Casey turned and walked out the door, closing it behind him. Cathleen stumbled to her bed and sank onto it, stunned.

Chapter 8

IT SEEMED HOURS BEFORE HER BODY STOPPED TREMBLING AND
Cathleen was able to breathe normally. When her brain
began to function again, embarrassment washed over her.
How could she face Casey? He had felt her passionate
response, and knew she had been his for the taking. Only
his good sense had stopped them, not hers. She had been
out of control, completely under his spell. The idea of
losing command of herself was abhorrent to Cathleen.
Casey had far too much power over her. After what had
happened a few minutes earlier, he was certain to realize
it. And certain to use it.

Cathleen rose and walked to the mirror to stare at her
face. It was flushed with desire, her eyes huge and so dark
blue that they were almost black. Her mouth was red-
dened and swollen from the force of their kisses. Hers was
the face of a woman pulled from her lover's arms: soft with
hunger, yet taut with lack of fulfillment. Wonderingly
Cathleen touched her tender lips. She looked almost
beautiful.

What was she to do? Go to bed with C.J. Casey? Lay herself open to all the hurt that might follow? Take her place in a bed women far more experienced than she had lost? It was crazy. Absolutely insane. Casey could crush her heart and soul.

Yet if she continued to see Casey, that would be the result. Eventually he would make love to her. He'd made it painfully obvious that he could persuade her to do almost anything. And if they made love, Cathleen knew she would fall in love with him. She already teetered on the edge of that disaster. Being in love with someone like Casey was the last thing she needed. He was too much like her father. There would be jealousy, fights, suspicion, drunken accusations—no, she'd sworn that her life would never be like that. She couldn't allow it. Yet that was what waited at the end of a relationship with Casey.

Cathleen clenched her hands and turned away. For several minutes she paced the carpet, sliding her hands up and down each other. It didn't help. Finally she willed her mind to stop its crazy, jumbled turning. She sat down before the mirror and combed her hair, smoothing it into its usual neat cap. Then she concentrated on applying her makeup, blanking out all thoughts. When she was through she rose and pulled a pair of hose from her drawer. She put them on and slipped her feet into strappy white sandals. Like a woman in shock, she moved mechanically, transferring things from the purse she had used the night before to a white handbag. She stopped and wet her lips. The automatic acts of getting ready to go out steadied her nerves and gave her a little time to restore her outward calm. A glance in the mirror told her that she looked in possession of herself. Only she would know how strongly she was quaking inside. She drew in a deep breath. The moment of decision had come. Did she dare tempt fate by going out with Casey?

It was too risky, she thought, but the idea brought an immediate ache to her chest, and a voice inside her head taunted, "Coward." Cathleen shoved her handbag under

her arm, and her outthrust chin tilted determinedly.
Whatever else might be said of Dusty and Stella, surely
they hadn't turned out a daughter who was a coward.
Cathleen strode to the door and opened it, then swept
down the hall to the den.

Casey was waiting for her on the couch, stretched out
with his heels up on one sofa arm, his dark head flat on the
other end. His eyes were closed and his arms crossed over
his stomach. He looked deflatingly relaxed. "All you need
is a lily in your hands," Cathleen quipped as she stepped
into the room.

His eyes opened and Cathleen fought the blush that
flooded her cheeks when his gaze touched her. "Watch it,"
he warned vaguely, swinging his feet onto the floor and
sitting up. "I've done my good deed for the day. From now
on it's open season."

Cathleen tossed him a scornful look, ignoring the sudden speeding up of her pulse. He slid one arm around her
shoulders and guided her out of the house to his car. As
they drove downtown, Casey kept up a casual flow of
conversation and Cathleen's nervousness subsided. He
stopped on a narrow street in an old part of downtown.
Many of the buildings were large warehouses, Cathleen
guessed. But the building they entered was thin and tall, a
red-and-brown brick structure decorated with carved
stone between each story.

Again Casey draped his arm around her shoulders as
they walked into the building and up the flight of stairs,
their bodies brushing together at hips and chest. Cathleen
was tensely aware of each step, each touch. On the second
floor Casey opened a heavy wooden door and stepped
back to let Cathleen enter first. She walked into a reception area completely at odds with the old, faded building.
The room was filled with sunlight and plants. Almost an
entire wall had been knocked out and reset with full-length
plate-glass windows. Pale, monochromatic furniture was
scattered about the room, so bland that it didn't detract
from the abundant greenery and the plush, vivid plum

carpet, yet quite tasteful, too. A girl sat behind an elegant writing table. She looked up at their entrance, and a broad smile lit her face. "Mr. Casey, how nice to see you. Ms. Chase said you would be in today."

"Hello." Cathleen was sure he couldn't remember the girl's name. He met too many people. But his smile and warm, direct gaze transmitted a sense of familiarity, even of intimacy, that would leave the secretary with the impression that he remembered her. It wasn't something Casey cultivated to impress or woo people. It was simply a part of his natural charm. To a large degree, Dusty had the same ability.

The thought disturbed her, and Cathleen turned away to sit down on one of the low-slung couches. Moments later the double doors leading into the inner rooms swept open dramatically and a woman emerged. "Casey! You old devil. I haven't seen you in ages!"

Casey, who had been gazing idly out the windows, turned, grinned and opened his arms to envelop the woman in a hug. "Liz. You know I can't stay away from you."

The woman chuckled, flattered by his banter. Cathleen stared at her in amazement. She had pictured the clothing designer as being sleek, sophisticated and perfectly groomed. Liz Chase was exactly the opposite. Squat and short, she wore a faded denim skirt and an old, plain blue blouse. Her long, gray-sprinkled hair was pulled back starkly into a bun. Three pencils were stuck into the sides of her hair, with the result that several strands had pulled loose and straggled down the side of her face. She wore no makeup, no nail polish, no jewelry and no shoes. Cathleen had never seen a plainer, more unadorned woman.

Liz pulled out of Casey's arms and pivoted to look at Cathleen. "Is this the girl?" she asked rhetorically.

Cathleen recovered her good manners enough to stand and smile. "Yes, I'm Cathleen Richards."

Liz Chase studied her figure with such thoroughness that Cathleen shifted uncomfortably. Cathleen could see Casey

standing behind the designer and smiling devilishly.
"Hmm," Liz commented at last. "You've got a very
interesting figure." She tilted her head and considered
Cathleen's face. "I really haven't the time, you know, but
I'll do you anyway. You're too good to miss."

She whirled abruptly and strode back into the inner
office. Cathleen turned to Casey. "Does that mean making
me look good is a challenge?"

Casey laughed. "Goose. Stop fishing for compliments.
Come on." He took her arm and followed Liz. The inner
room was obviously her studio: large, bare except for a
couple of easels and a few necessities, flooded with light
from the bank of windows. As he closed the door behind
them Casey leaned down to whisper in Cathleen's ear.
"She means you're gorgeous, and it'll be a pleasant change
to dress someone with a beautiful complexion and perfect
figure."

"Flatterer." But his words warmed her.

Liz picked up a small yellow pad from her cluttered
desk. "Tell me about your tour. How many cities and
days?"

Cathleen described the four-week tour and the number
of stops. Next Liz questioned her regarding costume
changes each night and, to her surprise, asked about the
style of her music. Cathleen wound up singing a couple of
her songs for the designer. Liz perched on her desk, eyes
closed, listening. Cathleen glanced at Casey in dismay, but
he merely nodded reassuringly. Liz scribbled a few notes
on her pad and finally took Cathleen's measurements.
Cathleen stood stiffly as the woman wound the measuring
tape around various parts of her body, embarrassed by
Casey's appreciative gaze that followed Liz's movements.

"Anything special you want to wear?" Liz asked.

"No. As you can probably tell, I haven't thought about
costumes."

"It shouldn't be hard to fix you up. You're pretty and
young and you have a figure that'll stop them dead in their
tracks. The only problem will be keeping you from looking

too short-waisted or too tarty. That's an easy mistake with a full figure, you know. But you'll give me a chance to use clean lines without frills and furbelows. When's your tour?"

When Cathleen told her, Liz grimaced. "Give me a week, and I'll have the designs for you to see."

Shortly afterward, Cathleen and Casey left.

Casey called Cathleen a couple of times during the week, but he didn't come to see her, and Cathleen thought he had decided that she wasn't worth the effort. She hated to admit how much she missed his easy, wry humor and husky voice, or how often she lay awake at night, remembering the glide of his long, rough fingers on her skin.

When the phone rang the next Wednesday morning it was Casey's rich voice on the other end of the line. "Hello, darlin'."

Cathleen's heart jumped, and her palms were suddenly damp with sweat. She struggled to keep her voice calm. "Hi, Casey."

"When should I pick you up?"

"What?"

"Have you forgotten? You're supposed to look at Liz's designs today."

"No, I haven't forgotten."

"When do you want to go?" he asked patiently.

"Casey, don't feel obligated to take me. I can find the place myself."

"Don't worry. I rarely do anything out of a sense of obligation. My mother always told me I was the most selfish person alive."

"Oh, really? Why did you convince John Metcalf to listen to Dusty?" she countered.

"Haven't you realized that it was just the first step in capturing that luscious body of yours?"

"Casey . . ."

"Okay, okay, no teasing. I owed Dusty for what he'd done for me. That was a way to pay him back, a way he would accept, which could have been hard to find otherwise. But I feel no obligation to lead you to Liz Chase's studio again. I simply have a healthy curiosity to see what she's cooked up for you—and a probably unhealthy desire to be with you."

A bubble of excitement formed in Cathleen's throat. She wanted to giggle for no reason. "Why unhealthy?"

"Didn't anybody ever tell you that abstinence causes terrible physical problems for a man?"

This time she couldn't repress the giggle. "Yeah, lots of guys." She clutched the phone, grinning sappily at the opposite wall. "But none of them ever died of it, as I recall."

"Maybe I'll be the first. I could catch pneumonia from the cold showers I have to take after I see you."

"I'll cry at your funeral."

"Cathleen Richards, you've got a cold heart, did you know that?"

"So I've been told."

His voice turned low and serious. "Cath, I've been staying away from you for a few days because I thought it might keep me from wanting you so much. It hasn't. I just think about you all the time." Cathleen's hand clenched the receiver, and she wet her dry lips. "I figured I might as well throw myself back into the fire. I want to see you again. Let me take you to Liz's."

"All right." She could manage little more than a whisper. She wondered if Casey knew how his words affected her. Did he realize that she was melting over here? He was so experienced at love games, and she was not. Had his absence the last week been a calculated strategy to make her want him? If so, he had certainly succeeded.

"When?"

"Give me an hour."

"Okay, I'll be there. Oh, Cathleen, wear something sexy, would you?"

He hung up. She replaced the receiver and walked back to her bedroom, strangely stirred by his last statement.

Maybe he was playing games. . . . Yet there had been an underlying tone of raw hunger to his bantering request. Wear something sexy, huh? She opened her closet door and studied her clothes. She didn't have anything sexy. Her choice in attire was usually designed to downplay her figure rather than accentuate it. Something sexy. A devil teased at the back of her mind. Casey had probably been kidding her about her typically unsexy clothes. Well, she would show him. A dreamy smile curved her lips as she contemplated his reaction to what she now planned to wear.

She hung up the tailored pants suit she'd gotten out earlier. She climbed up on a chair to pull down a box of old clothes she had put aside to give to the Salvation Army and dug through it until she found an old pair of jeans that had been washed too many times. They were faded and had so many tears and holes that she had cut them off to ragged shorts a couple of years earlier. The multitudinous washings had thinned the denim and shrunk them until they were far too tight. Cathleen stepped into the shorts and pulled them up. She had to suck in her breath to start the zipper, and after she managed to fasten them, they clung like a second skin, molding softly to her derriere.

Next she pulled out a ribbed halter that was bright pink and flattering to her coloring, but too small across the bosom for her tastes. Now she tried it on and turned to look at herself in the mirror. She couldn't have worn anything that would emphasize her figure more. The waistband of the shorts cinched her small waist. Her hips strained against the denim beneath. Above the shorts, there was a band of naked skin before the soft halter curved to fit her breasts. When she saw her image in the mirror, Cathleen's courage wavered. She was tempted to change clothes.

But the same nagging devil made her imagine Casey's eyes turning dark and hot when he saw her, and his mouth pulling down at the corners, one finger coming up to smooth his mustache. She tingled all over. Let him get what he asked for, she thought, ignoring the dichotomy of her feelings. She refused to think past the fact that she wanted to wear this outfit and see his reaction.

Casey's response was all she could have hoped for. When she opened the front door at his ring he stared at her without moving, his eyes dropping rapidly to her breasts, then downward. More slowly his gaze came back up, caressing each part of her. When his eyes finally came to rest on her face she saw the slackness of his mouth and the eager glitter of his black pupils, pinpoints in his pale blue irises. "You took me at my word," he murmured.

Cathleen swallowed, her abdomen turning to wax before his stare. She knew it had been stupid to bait him with these clothes, but she couldn't work up a decent regret. With trembling fingers she picked up her purse from the counter and joined him on the tiny side porch. He stepped back barely enough to let her by, and the tips of her breasts brushed his chest. Cathleen thought she heard a funny little inrush of breath from him, but she ignored it and scampered down the concrete steps. He followed, staying behind by several steps. She glanced around inquisitively.

"Just enjoying the view," he explained, his eyes glued to her hips. Cathleen blushed, and the blood seemed to converge in her stomach, turning to fire there and spreading back out.

Casey didn't touch her as he opened the car door for her. He drove to Liz's studio with both hands conscientiously on the wheel. At every stoplight, however, his gaze turned to her, and the heat from his eyes was as tangible as a caress. Cathleen wondered why she had thought she melted at his words on the telephone. Her feeling then was nothing compared to the heat which swept through her now.

They didn't talk on the way to the studio. Cathleen found it difficult to concentrate on anything but the sight of his hands curved around the steering wheel, or the softened, almost sleepy set of his face when he turned to look at her. They arrived at Chase's and went up the stairs without touching, Casey falling in behind her. Cathleen was very aware of the view she gave him as she preceded him in her tight shorts. When they stepped inside the reception area Cathleen strolled to the window with all the casualness she could muster. Casey followed and bent to whisper in her ear, his breath evoking little shivers all through her body. "I can't decide whether to stand in front of you or behind."

She glanced up, puzzled, then caught his meaning. Her eyes widened a little, and she flushed. She licked her lips nervously, and Casey's eyes focused on the movement, as alert and quick as a cat watching its prey.

"Thank you for dressing like I asked," he went on in the same low murmur, "but you must know you've sealed your fate."

"I don't understand."

"Don't you?" His grin was lazy and sizzling with meaning. "There's no question now that you'll end up in my bed. I haven't touched you yet because I know that once I do, I won't be able to stop."

She caught her underlip with her teeth, her eyes widening. He sucked in his breath. "Keep that up and I won't even have to touch you to explode."

Liz Chase had to call them twice before either one was aware that she had entered the room. Reluctantly they joined her in the large studio. She led them to one of the easels, and flipped back the cover, revealing the first of her many sketches. Cathleen studied the designs, recognizing their beauty and striking effect, but unable to concentrate on them with Casey standing so close behind her.

Liz explained the different styles she had chosen, pointing out the less striking, softer designs she had picked for the smaller rural shows, noting the country touch she had added here and there. Cathleen murmured her delight, balking at only one, a simple black pants outfit. It was one piece and accented only by a rhinestone-buckled belt around the waist. "Are you sure this will look all right on me?" she questioned doubtfully.

"I knew you'd say that. Don't worry. It'll be perfect."

"Won't it make me look like a sack of potatoes?"

Liz guffawed. "Hardly. You aren't tall, but you aren't that short, either, and you have a perfectly delectable waist. Show it off. Most women would kill for a waist like yours."

"It's not the waist I object to," Cathleen retorted good-humoredly. "It's the hips."

"They're lovely hips." Liz patted the side of Cathleen's hips lightly, startling her. "Just look at Casey here. He's practically salivating."

"Your dresses are gorgeous, Liz, as always." Casey's smile was as slow and appealing as ever, but Cathleen detected a scratchy, impatient undertone to his voice.

"And you wish I'd get through so you can take Cathleen home, huh?" Liz twinkled. "Okay, I get the hint." She turned toward Cathleen inquiringly.

"I'll leave it in your hands," Cathleen told her. "You know more about it than I do. I like the drawings very much."

"Good." Liz beamed. "I'll call you when it's time for the first fitting."

"Can you get them done in time?"

"They'll be ready, I promise. I've been known to throw tantrums when something's late."

Liz looked so solid, so placid, that Cathleen had to smile at the idea that she would throw a tantrum about anything. Cathleen hesitated, sure there must be something else she should do or say. It was too major a decision to be made this quickly. Yet she had loved the clothes on sight, despite her uncertainty over the black jumpsuit, and she had to have costumes for the shows. Creating an image was an important part of any concert. Though extravagant-seeming, the elegant clothes were a necessary expense.

"Ready?" Casey asked, edging toward the door.

"Yes, I guess so." They said good-bye to Liz, who was already absorbed in the drawings before they left the room, and walked through the reception area and down the stairs to their car. Casey started the engine and stepped on the accelerator, and the sleek auto bolted forward. It was some minutes before Cathleen realized that Casey had passed the exit ramp he should have taken to reach her home. "Where are we going?"

"Franklin. I thought I'd show you my house."

Cathleen tensed. The moment of truth had arrived, precipitated by her foolish decision to wear something sexy. "Your house?"

"Yeah. You've never been there, have you?"

"No."

"It's a nice place. I have a stable of quarter horses. A pool if you'd like to go swimming. Or we could practice our song for Dusty's banquet. There's a studio where I work. The acoustics are good."

But none of those are the reason we're going there, Cathleen thought, not daring to say it aloud. She didn't want the sexual tension between them put into words. It would make it too real, too close. Too frightening. She stared out the window at the outer fringes of Nashville flashing past. This was the same expressway she had taken when she visited Dusty at the Villa. But all the times her stomach had tied in knots going out to see her father couldn't compare to the jittering, jangling nerves in her midsection now. Dread and excitement. Fear and anticipation. She wondered if this was how Dusty felt when he yearned for a drink—wanting something so bad you felt driven, yet terrified of the consequences.

Casey's farm was a few miles southeast of Franklin. It was surrounded by a high wire fence, which he explained was electrified. Cathleen turned a startled face toward him. "You need that much protection?"

Casey shrugged as he stopped before the massive iron gates and opened them with a remote-control unit. "It's a working farm. My horses are expensive, and there are a few things worth stealing in the house. Occasionally a maniac threatens to kill me." They entered the tree-lined drive winding to his house, and the gates swung to behind the car.

Cathleen gasped. "You're kidding."

He shook his head. "Things have changed since Dusty was at the top of the heap. Fans aren't the only ones who try to get to you anymore. There's always a joker who thinks he'll make a big name for himself by shooting someone famous. Most of the letters aren't serious. But who would have figured anyone would shoot John Lennon? I don't care for the idea of bodyguards, so I settled for that fence and a few Dobermans to prowl the grounds at night."

Cathleen frowned. "I shouldn't be surprised. When I was eight Dusty hired a bodyguard to escort Lynette and me to school because he'd received a kidnapping threat."

"There are always loonies around. You can't do anything except take reasonable precautions and then forget about it. I can't live looking over my shoulder. What good's my money if that's what I have to pay for it? Stella has round-the-clock guards at her house, and she doesn't set a foot outside it without another bodyguard along."

"You mean that guy's really her bodyguard? I thought that was a euphemism for her—" Cathleen stopped in midsentence, embarrassed.

"Her lover?" Casey completed quizzically. "Boy, you sure don't have a high opinion of your mother, do you?"

"It was a little hard to after the divorce trial."

"When you take two human beings and slice them open in court, it's difficult for either one to come out looking good. Divorce is vicious. Dusty's lawyer portrayed Stella as a nymphomaniac, and Stella's made Dusty look like a drunken, abusing bastard."

"She ripped him apart to get his money. She wasn't fighting for custody of her children." Cathleen's voice was low, almost trembling, laced with years-old pain. "She gave Lynette and me to Dusty quick as a wink. In return she took all his assets."

Casey reached out to touch her lustrous dark hair. "I'm sorry you were hurt. Sixteen's a hard age to find out how fallible one's parents are."

"Oh, I knew it before then. Dusty was a drunk and had a dreadful temper. His rages used to terrify Lynette."

"Not you?"

"A little. Usually they made me furious. I can't tell you how many nights Dusty and I argued. But at least I knew he loved us. Stella was another story. She wasn't scary, but I realized pretty young that she cared about herself and Dusty, in that order. Lynette and I came way down on the list."

Casey stopped the car and turned toward Cathleen. His voice was soft as satin, and his fingers tangled in her hair with equal gentleness. "I wish I could take the hurt from you."

She smiled up at him, her eyes swimming with tears. "Thank you. You're very sweet, Casey."

Her face was soft and vulnerable, with no defenses. A fierce protectiveness swelled in Casey's chest, yet at the same time desire licked through him. He wanted to pull her to him and kiss her thoroughly, but he knew that if he did, he wouldn't make it to the house. The bittersweet protective urge inside him wouldn't allow anything but the best and gentlest setting for their first lovemaking. "I want you, Cathleen," he whispered, his voice made ragged by his restraint. "More than anything in the world. If you'll let me, I want to make love to you this afternoon—and this evening and all through the night. But I refuse to harm you or bully you into it. It has to be your free choice. If you want me to take you back, just tell me." A crooked grin split his face. "God knows, I won't want to, but I'll do it."

Cathleen stared at Casey. He was forcing her to decide. He wouldn't ease her into it by seducing her. She had to make a clear and conscious consent, not agree in the midst of hazy pleasure. Her brain was drumming out a refusal, but the instinct which had made her wear this outfit pushed her toward him. So what if it wasn't smart? It was what she wanted. Admit it. Grab at the chance for happiness, however brief. Frightened as she was, Cathleen wanted to taste the nectar Dusty and Stella had drunk, to fly high and free in the airy regions of love. No thought of the pain. No dread of disaster. Casey was offering her a taste of heaven, and she had to take it, whatever hell might follow.

"I don't want you to take me home," she told him softly. "I want to stay with you."

Chapter 9

A LIGHT FLICKERED IN CASEY'S EYES AND WAS GONE. WITH slow, precise movements he switched on the ignition and put the car into gear. He didn't speak. His hands assumed a death grip on the steering wheel. The muscles in his arms bunched under the pressure, and Cathleen stared at them, fascinated by the smooth curve and dip of his flesh. Her eyes followed the line of his arm to his hand, noting the sprinkling of fine black hairs on his brown skin, the bulge of veins against the tender skin of his inner elbow, and the bony knob at his wrist. Casey's body was excitingly masculine, she thought, but not animalistic, with an overabundance of hair, or muscles that were too developed.

The house came into sight. Low and swooping, with straight clean lines, it sprawled across the top of a small rise, dominating the land and buildings around. It was modernistic in design and consisted almost entirely of wood and glass. "It's lovely!" Cathleen exclaimed.

She stepped out of the car and started up the terraced

path to the front door. Casey followed her, one hand
barely grazing the small of her back. She remembered his
words. *"Once I touch you, I won't be able to stop."* Now he
knew he wouldn't have to stop. The thought sent a long
shiver through her.

The front door had no key, but opened to a computer
code that Casey tapped out on a small plate beside the
doorbell. "I like gadgets," he explained with a self-
deprecating smile.

Cathleen chuckled. "Don't apologize. I grew up with
some of the flashiest *nouveau-riche* decor around. You're a
model of conservative good taste compared to some of the
things Dusty's done."

"Yeah. I remember the doorbell at your old house."

Cathleen burst into laughter. "You mean the one that
played the first eight bars of 'Greenwood'?"

"The same." He pushed open the door and let her pass
him into the hall. The entry was wide, offering a clear view
of the large living area and the bank of windows dominating it. Cathleen pulled in her breath sharply at the vista
framed by the windows: a sparklingly white stable and
barn trimmed in red, beyond them white-fenced paddocks
and, in the distance, rolling tree-covered land.

"Oh, Casey, it's beautiful." She crossed the quarry tile
of the entry, cushioned by an oriental area rug, and
walked to the far windows. Only after a long, slow look at
the view did she turn to survey the rest of the room. It was
a masculine area, sparingly furnished with large, comfortable pieces. The wall at one end was centered by a huge
stone fireplace. On the mantle above it stood several small
pieces of sculpture. On a table beside the couch was an
abstract bronze piece. The other walls held large, colorful
paintings. Even from a distance Cathleen could see that
the sculptures were beautiful, and she recognized several
of the paintings as the work of a Caribbean artist whose
bright, almost primitive style had become popular during
the last few years. So that was what Casey meant when he
said there were a few things worth stealing in the house.

They were indeed worth stealing. As part of her music

major in college Cathleen had been required to take several art appreciation and art history courses. She knew enough about the subject to realize that the art in this room alone must be worth a fortune. She wouldn't have dreamed that Casey was a collector of such taste. "Do you collect art as an investment?" she asked, turning from her contemplation of the pictures.

"Not really. My financial manager tells me I should, but I buy what appeals to me, like those Maregny oils. I bought them before he hit it big."

"You have excellent taste."

"Not what you'd expect from an old country boy, huh?" He grinned. "Didn't you know I come from a deplorable background for a country and western singer?"

"No. What?"

His eyes danced. "My father was a doctor, and a Yankee, to boot. He moved south because he had a rheumatic condition which was worsened by cold weather. I grew up in a resort town in Florida and spent most of my youth at swimming pools or in the ocean."

"Casey, you're a fraud!" she teased. "All that 'good old boy' Southern charm . . ."

"I'm Southern," he protested. "I just come from bad blood. The accent's real. Whatever charm I possess is indisputably natural. My family said my manners were deplorable."

"And that you were selfish," she reminded him.

"That too. I'd lie on my bed playing the guitar instead of carrying out the trash or mowing the lawn."

"Sounds like normal teenage behavior to me."

"Not according to my mother. My stepmother, actually. My natural mother split when I was a baby. Apparently I got my musical ability and wild nature from her. I sure as hell didn't get them from Dad. He was as starchy as the second woman he married. Frankly, I liked my stepmother better than I liked him. Dad was always gone, catering to rich old biddies in poor health, raking in the dough." He broke off and made a light gesture. "Enough of my family history. You want to see the rest of the house?"

"Yes, please." His description of his family had stirred Cathleen's compassionate nature. She was warmed by his revealing something that had obviously hurt him. Casey wasn't typically a disclosing sort of man. She ached for him, feeling his pain herself. She could readily understand why he wanted to dismiss the subject.

Casey led her down a hall that ran perpendicular to the entry and main room. "This is the dining room. I never eat in there. Down here are most of the bedrooms and baths." Self-consciously Cathleen peeked into four spacious, airy bedrooms and three large baths, wondering which one was Casey's room. None seemed like him. As if he could read her mind, he went on. "These are the guest bedrooms. Mine's back this way." They retraced their steps to the opposite wing, passing a modernistic kitchen fully equipped with all kinds of gadgets. Cathleen itched to get into it and try out the equipment, but Casey pulled her on.

The next room was large and contained little furniture, only a comfortable-looking sofa and an equally pleasant chair. Two walls were lined with plate-glass windows looking out on the front drive. A classic baby grand piano sat near one window with the light pouring onto its keys. In a corner of the room stood a table littered with sheets of music, pencils and paper. Another wall held a large, closed oak cabinet. This was obviously Casey's music room, the place where he practiced and ground out his songs.

He gestured toward the windows. "That's so I can see who's coming up the drive and duck out."

Cathleen smiled. "Likely story. I saw those gates, remember?"

"Sometimes I give other people one of the openers." His eyelids drooped, darkening his eyes. He came closer and placed his hands, palms flat, on either side of her arms. Lightly his hands slid up to her shoulders and down again. "There are people I want to have free access."

"Are you trying to ply me with an electric gate opener?" Cathleen struggled for a light, teasing tone. The effect of his hands touching her bare arms was devastating.

"With anything I can think of," he murmured in reply, watching the course of his hands. His fingers stopped at her shoulders, circling them with great care. Cathleen felt her bones cracking and dissolving, leaving her limp. She sagged, closing her eyes.

"Casey, I . . . I don't think I can stand up much longer," she whispered.

His breath rasped in harshly, and he bent to scoop her up in his arms. "Oh, Cathy, Cathy . . ." He nuzzled the sensitive skin along the side of her neck, and she moved her head to allow him more room to explore. He responded with soft, nibbling kisses that seared her skin and turned her liquid with desire. She felt the tremor of his arms against her back and knew the strength of his banked passion.

Casey carried her out of the music room and crossed the wide hall to his bedroom. Cathleen caught a quick impression of a large room filled with tree-filtered light before he laid her down on his bed. The bedspread was dark blue, with the sheen of satin, sinfully luxurious upon her skin. Casey sat beside her on the bed. For a long moment he simply looked at her. Then he began the familiar, delightful stroking of her arms, but this time his hands continued over her shoulders and down the front of her shirt, curving over her breasts. "I've been waiting weeks to do this." His voice was uneven.

He spread his hands over her breasts, his long fingers encompassing them gently. Cathleen's face flamed red. She felt shy and unbearably excited all at the same time. Her nipples puckered, shamelessly stretching the thin haltertop. He caressed the peaks with his forefingers, watching them thicken and elongate as if reaching for his caress.

Casey took her breast in his mouth, soaking the cloth as his tongue stroked the hard button. At last he pulled away and softly blew on the wet spot. The contrast of the sudden coolness on her heated skin sent a jolt straight through her, exploding in her abdomen. He continued the play of his mouth on her other nipple, and even though she was prepared this time for the parting breath of air, desire quivered through her as sharply as before.

Casey stood up. His eyes steadily on her body, he jerked at the buttons of his shirt, cursing softly when one refused to budge. He whipped off his shirt, and Cathleen eyed his naked chest shamelessly. His chest wasn't thick, but the tanned skin was molded over ridges of taut muscle. The plateau of his ribcage dropped off into the flat, softer plain of his stomach. Shyly Cathleen reached out to touch him, barely grazing her fingers across his stomach. His muscles quivered beneath her touch.

Then he unbuckled his belt. Even the sight of his hand sliding the metal prong from its fastener was sensual and stirring. Cathleen closed her eyes, delighting in the soft, identifiable sounds of his undressing: the soft swoosh as his belt slid through its loops, the rasp of a zipper, the clink of change and keys in the pants pockets as his jeans hit the floor, the successive thuds of his boots. The bed sagged beside her with his weight, and she opened her eyes.

Casey bent to kiss her mouth. His tongue eased in sinuously, familiarly, and Cathleen's tongue welcomed it. Their friction was achingly soft and lengthy. Casey's breath shuddered out through his nose, hot and impatient, while his tongue teased and danced with all the patience and leisure imaginable. His mobile lips skillfully worked on hers, demanding, asking, teasing, fervent, while his tongue continued its possession. Cathleen smoothed her hands over his bare arms and shoulders, delighting in the heat and firmness of his flesh. Casey stirred and shifted his body so that it pressed against hers all over, branding her with his heat and leaving her in no doubt as to the strength of his desire.

Cathleen dug in her heels and arched against his weight, barely moving him but vaulting his passion higher. Casey groaned and pulled away. He reached down to take the hem of her shirt in his hands and inched it upward to reveal her flesh. Cathleen moved restlessly, suddenly yearning to view his face as he looked at her nakedness. She sat up to allow him to pull the halter over her head, and her ripe breasts swung free. Casey swallowed convulsively. "Beautiful. So beautiful."

She lay back on the bed, the smooth spread erotic under her naked skin, intensifying the sensual pleasure of Casey's touch. He covered her breasts with his hands, exploring their softness and the contrasting pebbled nipples. The tip of each finger grazed over her nipples and in ever-widening circles on her breasts. Cathleen's abdomen was heavy and aching, as if all her blood had settled there. She shifted, seeking a more comfortable position, but there was none. Casey's eyelids lowered a fraction, and a sleepy smile touched his lips. He slipped one hand between her legs and pressed against their meeting place. His hand burned through the cloth of her jeans. She clamped her legs around it, urging him closer.

With one hand arousing her, he lowered his head to one breast and sucked the nipple into his mouth. Cathleen made a small noise of surprised pleasure, and he increased the suction, pulling until it was almost painful, then relaxing and laving the tip with a soothing tongue. His free hand took the other nipple between forefinger and thumb, rolling and stroking, until Cathleen almost sobbed with the combined pleasure of the three places he touched. Her legs twisted and opened helplessly as she dug her fingers into his back.

Casey groaned and lifted his head. His agile fingers went to the fastening of her denim shorts. He soon had them undone and pulled them down her legs, exposing the lacy pink panties beneath. His hand returned to caress the mound of her femininity, now separated from her skin by only the flimsy lace and nylon. His mouth began to taste her other breast. Cathleen luxuriated in the sensations rising again in her as Casey moved her closer and closer to the brink. She blushed to feel her own response, but Casey reveled in it, slipping his fingers beneath the trim of her underwear to feel her damp warmth more fully.

Roughly he pulled the scrap of cloth from her, and his mouth moved down her body, pausing to investigate the well of her navel, then continuing lower. Cathleen's breath

came in gasps as his tongue tickled the sensitive flesh of
her inner thighs, his hands parting her legs and stroking
the outsides as he bathed the inner skin with his tongue.
He murmured brokenly and moved back up, supporting
his weight on his forearms as he took his place between her
legs and eased into her. Cathleen tangled her fingers in his
thick black hair and pulled his face down for a kiss. His
tongue took her mouth in hot imitation of his bodily
possession of her. With infinite slowness he began to move
in the rhythms of love.

Casey dragged his mouth away from hers, frantically
kissing her face and neck, her name spilling agitatedly
from his lips. Cathleen pressed upward, seeking satisfaction, and her hands slid down to dig into his hips. Her
action tore a groan from him, and he began to thrust
harder and faster, hurtling Cathleen into the far realms of
pleasure. She gasped as shock waves of joy coursed
through her. She wrapped her arms around him convulsively. Her pleasure spurred his, and Casey shuddered,
uttering a short, incoherent cry against her skin.

Slowly they relaxed, returning to sanity. His breathing
slowed, and he rolled his weight off her, pulling her into
the crook of his arm and cuddling her to his side. Cathleen
settled her head in the hollow of his shoulder, too adrift in
pleasure to speak or even think. In that moment she knew
only Casey: the dampness of his flesh, his warmth, the
musky scent of their lovemaking. The rest of the world
ceased to exist.

Casey whispered her name and brushed his lips against
her hair. She smiled and rubbed her cheek against his
sleek skin. "You're a beautiful, beautiful woman," he told
her huskily. "I think I could spend my life making love to
you."

"It might get a little boring, don't you think?" Cathleen
teased softly.

"I don't know. I wouldn't mind finding out." Casey let
out a satisfied sigh. With one hand he stroked her bare
arm.

For a long time they remained in bed, giggling and

murmuring, loath to leave the intimacy they shared. But finally Casey's stomach rumbled with hunger, dragging them back to the real world. They rose and dressed, then ambled into the kitchen. Casey made a cursory inspection of the shelves and refrigerator. "Looks like eggs and toast. How does that sound?"

"Great." Cathleen's voice was soft and rich with love. She had shoved her worries and doubts into a corner of her mind and locked them away. She was going to enjoy this time without analyzing or worrying. The big step had been taken. There was no drawing back. She might as well enjoy it and leave the worrying for later.

"What are you thinking about?" Casey asked as he took out a small mixing bowl and cracked an egg against the side.

"You," Cathleen answered honestly, and he smiled.

"Careful. I might begin to think you liked me."

Cathleen grimaced in response. "I've always wanted to be able to do that." She nodded toward the mixing bowl.

"What?" he turned, surprised.

"Crack eggs with one hand."

"It's quite a skill," he joked. "If you're good, I'll teach you sometime."

"What if I'm bad?"

He grinned, his eyes flickering assessingly over her body. "That might be even better."

A treacherous warmth took root in her. Even a mildly suggestive phrase from his lips had the power to shake her. He went back to his culinary tasks, adding a dollop of milk to the eggs and whisking them to a froth. He put a lump of butter in a skillet and set it on one of the electric coils to heat. As he waited, he pulled out a block of cheese from the refrigerator and set it on the center island beside a built-in food processor. Cathleen watched him idly, enjoying the sight of his quick, sure fingers preparing the meal. He poured the egg and milk mixture into the skillet, adding dashes of several herbs, and scrambled them. As a finishing touch he scattered the cheese he'd grated in the food processor over the eggs.

"Don't tell me you made that," Cathleen protested as he pulled a chunk of uncut bread from the copper breadbox.

Casey laughed, showing straight, white teeth, and Cathleen's stomach sizzled again. "No. My housekeeper baked it yesterday."

"Oh. Is she here today?"

"No. It's her day off." He sliced the bread and popped it into the toaster, then set out jars of jams and jellies on the counter. "What kind of jam do you like?" He began to reel off flavors.

"Whoa. Stop. I don't want any jam, thank you. Where'd you get all those flavors?"

He shrugged. "Presents, mostly. Don't you get all those gift packages from people at Christmas?"

"Not in that quantity."

"Everybody who wants to sell me something sends me those things. I throw half the stuff away." He dished up the eggs and toast, and set the plates on the butcher-block kitchen table. "I don't have any orange juice. I have coffee, though. Want some?"

"Plain water will be fine." Cathleen took a bite of her eggs. "Mmm, these are delicious. Tell me, do you always have breakfast in the afternoon?"

"Nope. Sometimes I have it in the morning." He leaned toward her confidentially. "It's pretty much the only thing I know how to cook."

"You do it well."

"Why, thank you, ma'am." He took her hand in one of his, curling his fingers around it. Cathleen discovered that she liked the feel of his long, rough fingers wrapped around hers.

She ate with her left hand, although it was a trifle awkward, so she could leave her other hand resting in Casey's. "Casey, I've been wondering. . . ."

"Yeah?"

"Were you—the other day when you said something about feeling you ought to pay Dusty back for his help and it was hard to find something he'd accept—well, did you pay for his stay at the Villa, too?"

"No. I didn't even know he was there until a few weeks before he left."

"Oh. It wasn't Jack either. I can't imagine who did it."

Casey hesitated. "I think I know who it was."

"Who?"

"You may not believe me."

"Who?"

"Your mother."

There was a dead silence. Cathleen's mouth twisted. "Come on, Casey."

"I told you you might not believe me."

"Why would Stella Farrow spend a nickel on Dusty's recovery?"

"Stella's not a bad lady, honey."

Cathleen rose, picking up her plate and carrying it to the sink to rinse. "That's always a man's opinion of her."

Casey sighed. "I don't want to argue with you. I started not to say it. You're terribly biased where your mother's concerned. It takes two to break up a marriage, you know."

"Dusty didn't want her to leave. He loved her. I think he still loves her."

"Maybe so. In some ways, I think Stella still loves him."

"Three husbands later?" Cathleen sneered.

"That's one evidence of it," he replied calmly. "Honey, Dusty contributed his share to their divorce. He was a boozer and a gambler back then, too. It didn't start after Stella left."

"I might have expected you to take her side." Cathleen's voice was as cold as her insides suddenly felt. "Are you still in love with her? Is that why you wanted me? Because I'm her daughter? Because I remind you of her?"

"Don't be stupid!" Casey jumped to his feet and strode to where she stood. He gripped her upper arms fiercely, his blue eyes blazing down at her. "I want you solely for yourself. In fact, you resemble Dusty more than Stella, and I certainly don't have any lurking desire to take him to bed!"

A reluctant smile curved her mouth. "I'm sorry. You must think I'm a bad-tempered, paranoid idiot."

"No. I think you're a young woman who was badly hurt by her mother and decided to shut away the hurt, the mother and everything connected to her. It's understandable—and maybe it's a good way to cope for a while. But someday you have to stop, or you'll be an embittered, regretful old lady." He took her hands in his and held them against his chest. She could feel the warmth of his skin through his shirt. It was somehow both soothing and exciting. "Don't you think you ought to at least see Stella?"

"No!" She jerked her hands away. "I will not see her. Don't think you can turn Stella and me into friends. We're long past any feeling for each other."

"I think you're wrong."

Cathleen's hands clenched together. The old aching hurt was rising in her stomach. She struggled to shove it back down. She was through with all that. Through with her mother. She wasn't about to let Casey sweet talk her into opening herself up to the pain again. "Could we talk about something else? Please?"

Casey took one look at her rigid posture and balled hands and sighed. "Sure. Would you like to see the grounds? The stables?"

"Okay."

He reached out, and she unfolded her fist to fit his hand. They left the house by the back door and strolled past the long swimming pool. The sun glittered on the water and was reflected against the tiles lining the inner rim. Cushioned redwood loungers were scattered around the pool invitingly. One table sported a brightly patterned umbrella, now folded. Cathleen thought of lying in one of the long chairs, reading and lazily soaking up the sun, Casey beside her reaching across the space between their chairs to clasp her hand. A warmth unlike her earlier passion spread through her. She wanted to be around him as much as she wanted the fire which had blazed between them this afternoon.

"There are the stables." Casey pointed to the white, red-trimmed frame building at the bottom of the slope.

"It's beautiful. Looks like something in Kentucky."

"Yes, except they're quarter horses. I race them out West."

"Have you had any winners?"

He glowed with pride. "Sure. Happy Moments, Ginger-snap, Millie's Pride . . ." He began to reel off a list of names and races which meant nothing to Cathleen. She enjoyed hearing him talk and watching the almost boyish happiness light up his face. They toured the stables, and Casey greeted the grooms by name, stopping to discuss one horse with the trainer. When Casey suggested to Cathleen that they ride, her mouth flew open in astonishment.

"Ride a racehorse? Me? Are you kidding? I haven't ridden a horse since that little Shetland pony Dusty gave us."

Casey laughed. "I can tell you don't know anything about horses. Robertson would have my head if we rode any of the horses I raise to race. But we have other mounts for pleasure riding. I'll find one to suit your experience."

"I doubt it. My experience would be hard to match."

Casey saddled a couple of horses and helped her mount, assuring her that her horse was thoroughly gentle. He was barely holding back his laughter, and Cathleen stuck out her tongue at him. He burst into laughter unabashedly.

"Oh, you!" Cathleen said in mock disgust.

He adjusted her stirrups, giving her a final pat on the ankle, and swung up into his own saddle. They set out at a calm walk as Casey turned in his saddle to explain a few rudiments of riding to Cathleen. After a few minutes of placidly swaying along she decided that he had given her a suitably calm steed, and she was able to relax and enjoy the ride. She asked a few questions about quarter horses and quarter horse racing. Casey was happy to oblige her with answers. The remainder of the afternoon passed easily, full of companionship and laughter. Cathleen didn't question the quiet content any more than she questioned the sudden flare of passion within her when Casey pulled the horses to a stop and kissed her, or when he made a double entendre and cast her a hot, meaningful look.

When the sun began to sink they turned back to the stables. Cathleen was sorry to see the afternoon end, but there was a tug of anticipation in her gut as she wondered what lay ahead for the evening. Casey left the horses in the charge of a groom, and they strolled to the house. "How about a shower?" he asked, the sparkle in his eye implying something more than a simple wash.

Cathleen's heartbeat picked up its pace, and a blush began in her cheeks. "I . . . I'd love one, but these are the only clothes I have."

His grin turned decidedly wicked. "That's okay. I'm sure I can find something appropriate for you to wear."

"Well . . ." She hesitated a moment just for the effect, casting her eyes downward shyly.

Casey's hand encircled her wrist. His voice was rich with amusement. "Don't quit singing for an acting career. You'll never make it."

She cast a teasing sideways glance at him. "Egotist."

"Coward," he replied softly, and pulled her to a halt. He gathered her into his arms and kissed her. There was none of the hungry demand of their earlier encounters, only promise and leisurely enjoyment. Finally he pulled back. "Stay with me, Cathleen. I want you in my bed all night long. I want to wake up tomorrow morning and see you beside me."

Everything inside her stirred at his appeal, emotionally and physically. It was what she wanted, too, but she hesitated, her mind going to Dusty. Would he be all right alone? "I—yes, I'd like to stay."

"Good." He smiled and kissed her again.

Pink cheeked and slightly flustered, Cathleen broke their kiss. "First . . ." Her breath was fluttery and her thoughts confused. "First I have to tell Dusty I'll be out all night. Otherwise he'll worry when I don't show up."

He grimaced, but released her. "Okay, mother hen. There's a phone on the nightstand in my bedroom."

They walked hand in hand into the bedroom. Casey proceeded to the bathroom, and she could hear him humming as he turned on the shower. With a thrill of happiness she realized that he was humming "Jody," one of her songs. She smiled and sat down on the bed to dial her home number. The phone rang only twice before it was picked up, but it was Jack Beaudry's whispery voice that answered, not Dusty's. "Jack? It's Cathleen. Is Dusty—"

"Cathy! Where have you been? We were worried sick about you."

"What? Oh. Sorry I didn't leave a note, but I didn't expect to be gone this long. I went to Chase's with Casey, and afterwards we decided to—"

There was a muffled noise at the other end of the line. Then her father's voice came on the line, more tense than she had heard it in a long time. "Baby, you better come home quick. All hell's broken loose here."

Chapter 10

FEAR SLICED THROUGH HER. FOR A MOMENT CATHLEEN couldn't catch her breath. Vague visions of disaster, all hinging on Dusty's return to drinking, swept through her head. Casey, who had reentered the room and was unbuttoning his shirt, stopped at the sight of her white face. "Cathy? Honey, what is it? What's the matter?"

Cathleen wet her lips and held up a hand to stop Casey's questions, shaking her head that she didn't know. "What are you talking about?" she managed to ask Dusty.

"Lynette's here, crying all over the place. She left her husband, says she's getting a divorce. She wants to move in for a while."

"Oh, no." With a pang of guilt Cathleen remembered her sister's hints about her marriage going bad. She had meant to visit Lynette and have a nice long talk about it, but with recording and the tour and Casey, she'd never gotten around to it. She had failed Lynette when she needed her.

"She's pretty upset, and I can't get any sense out of her. Come home and talk to her."

"I'll be there as soon as I can. Okay?"

"What is it?" Casey repeated as she hung up the phone. He came toward her.

Cathleen sighed and stood up. She ran her fingers through her hair and thought about how reluctant she was to go home. She would much rather spend the night in Casey's arms. The thought increased her guilt. "It's Lynette. Her marriage is in trouble. Apparently she's left Michael."

"You have to go home because of it?" He frowned in puzzlement. "Couldn't it wait until tomorrow?"

"No. I've already waited longer than I should have. I knew there was something wrong, but I didn't make the time to talk to Lynette. The least I can do is go home now. Maybe there's a chance to make it up before they're irreparably split."

"A few hours won't make any difference."

"It will to Lynette's well-being!" Cathleen lashed out, remorse and anxiety flaring into anger. "Are you being obtuse, or just selfish? My sister needs me, and that's more important than . . . than . . . cavorting in your shower!"

His face tightened. "She's your sister, not your child. You don't have to run every time she calls. She's a grown woman. She and her husband can work out their problem, if it's workable. Good Lord, Cathleen, are you responsible for everyone in the family?"

Cathleen's jaw jutted out, and tears welled in her eyes. How could he be so callous? Why didn't he understand? "I would like to go home. Please?"

Her voice was frigid and her posture unbending. Casey sighed, raking a hand through his hair. "Okay, okay. I'll drive you home. I'm sorry. I don't respond well to taking second place in your life."

Cathleen stared at him, too amazed to speak. She couldn't imagine Casey being concerned about his "place" in her life. She would have guessed that she was just one in a long string of women who had passed through this house, never to be seen or thought of again.

Casey stalked out of the bedroom and down the hall to

the front door, rebuttoning his shirt as he went. Cathleen followed, frowning. Emotional matters got so tangled. It would be easier if emotions had the precision and order of music. Then she would be able to deal with them. Inwardly she sighed, thinking she wasn't prepared to handle either Lynette's unhappiness or Casey's offended anger. She felt slightly sick to her stomach, wondering whether she had alienated Casey completely.

She slipped into the front seat of Casey's car and stole a glance at his tight-lipped countenance. Things didn't look good for her, she decided. Cathleen stared out the window, fighting the tears that threatened to overcome her. She couldn't let Casey see her cry. His gentle touch on her shoulder surprised her, and she jumped.

"I'm sorry," he began, his voice husky with emotion. "Here I am complaining about how you assume too much of everyone else's burdens, and then I add mine to the load. I spoke out of turn. I was frustrated and disappointed because I'd looked forward to tonight. You're right. I'm selfish. I didn't want to share you with anyone, including your family. But I know you want to help your sister. Your compassion and generosity are part of what's so appealing about you." His fingers slid down her arm to pick up her hand and carry it to his lips. His mustache tickled her palm. His mouth was warm, and the warmth seemed to shoot directly into her heart. Tears sprang into her eyes, and this time she was unable to control them.

"Oh, Casey." Her voice was low and choked. "It's not that you aren't important to me. But Lynette's in trouble. She depends on me. I have to be there when she needs me. Don't you see?"

"Yeah, I see. I see you giving everyone part of yourself." He grinned to ease the sting of his words. "I want all of you intact."

Cathleen's smile was watery. "Sometimes I wonder how much of you is real—and how much for show."

"I'm not complex, honey. I'm no Dusty Richards, with a hundred conflicting motives. I'm not this way today and another way the next time you see me. I don't put on acts, and most of the time I know who I am and what I want. Take me at face value."

She eyed him warily. "I guess I'm not a very trusting soul."

"Living with Dusty, that's a wise position to take." He tugged at her hand, and she slid across the seat to him. He curled one arm around her. Cathleen relaxed, letting her head rest on his shoulder. Apparently it hadn't blown apart after all. Despite Casey's flash of anger, he hadn't rejected her. The coiled spring in her chest unwound. The prospect of dealing with Lynette's problems suddenly didn't seem as dreary.

The driveway and the street in front of her house were clogged with expensive cars. Dusty's spanking new Cadillac, Jack's enormous Lincoln and a pale green Mercedes virtually filled the short driveway. Lynette's sporty little Datsun ZX was parked on the street in front of a sedate dark blue BMW. The cars looked odd around the small, inelegant frame house. "Has Dusty turned the place into a status car lot?" Casey remarked dryly as he maneuvered into a spot behind the BMW.

"The Lincoln is Jack Beaudry's. The Z belongs to Lynette. And I have a sinking feeling the owner of the BMW will turn out to be Michael Stokes. God knows who the other car belongs to."

"Jack picked a hell of a time to pay a visit."

Cathleen had to giggle. "Casey, honestly. This is serious."

"That's the best reason I can think of for finding the light side. Your problem is that you absorb everybody's feelings and make them your own. That's why you find it so difficult to deal with anything emotional. It hurts you too much. Try to remember that their problems are theirs, not yours. They made them, and they'll have to get out of them."

"That sounds very cynical."

"Just realistic. I've learned that you can't live another person's life for him."

They skirted the lawn and entered by the side door.

Raised voices sounded from the den. Cathleen glanced at Casey, drew a deep breath and headed for the noise, with him right behind her. They walked into confusion. Dusty was slumped in an easy chair, strumming on a guitar, his eyes closed as if to block out the people around him. Lynette and Michael were squared off, the length of a couch separating them, arguing in sharp voices that made Cathleen cringe inside. Jack was stalking across the room toward Michael, his body stiff and his hands shoved into his pockets. A woman stood beside Lynette, one arm around her shoulders, facing Michael defiantly. Everyone was talking loudly and concurrently, except Dusty. Cathleen stopped, her eyes fixed on the woman with Lynette. It was Stella Farrow.

Casey's arm slipped unobtrusively around Cathleen's shoulders. A long shiver passed through her. This was worse than she had expected. The angry voices reminded her far too vividly of Stella and Dusty's many fights, and for a moment she was a frightened child again. Casey tightened his arm, and the supportive gesture helped her to regain her perspective. She flashed him a grateful smile.

"Lynette?" Cathleen began in a normal tone. "Lynette, I'm home. Lynette!"

Nothing could be heard through the angry babble of voices. "Give me an answer!" Michael shouted and followed the order with a blunt expletive.

Jack's eyes shot fire, and he started toward Michael. "How dare you speak that way to her? I ought to—"

"I don't have to answer to you, or your family!" Lynette shrieked at the same time.

"Lynette doesn't want you here!" Stella chimed in. "Can't you see that? If you were any kind of a gentleman, you'd leave."

Jack was only a foot away from Michael now, looking harder and angrier than Cathleen had ever seen him. She thought despairingly that the two of them were about to come to blows. That was all they needed now—a brawl in the den. Then Casey lifted two fingers to his lips and uttered an ear-piercing whistle. The room fell silent immediately, and everyone swung toward them.

Jack Beaudry stared at Casey and Cathleen, his face strangely stunned, as if he'd just been hit in the stomach. Stella faced Cathleen silently, her back straight and proud, chin tilted up. Dusty bounded out of his chair with a vast sigh of relief. "Thank God, you're home."

"Cathy!" Lynette cried, pulling away from her mother and running to Cathleen.

Michael met her arrival with even greater relief than Dusty had. "Cathy! Maybe you can make some sense out of this. I haven't been able to get a straight word out of the whole bunch."

Cathleen felt a sudden cowardly urge to run, but she forced herself to stand her ground and take the sobbing Lynette into the circle of her arms. Instinctively she turned toward Casey, her eyes pleading. He didn't hesitate. He swung toward Dusty. "Why don't we get out and let Lynette talk to her sister. Jack? Stella?"

"Sure." Dusty accepted the invitation eagerly. He was no more eager to face problems than his eldest daughter was. Stella hesitated for a heartbeat, her eyes going to her two daughters. Then she nodded at Casey in acquiescence. Jack was the most reluctant to leave. He stared at Casey with something close to revulsion, then swung back to glare at Michael Stokes. Jerkily he moved away, nodding a short good-night to Dusty. He strode through the den into the hall and out the front door.

Casey herded the other two after Jack, pausing in the entryway to look at Cathleen. "Will you be okay alone?" His eyes went to Michael suspiciously.

Cathleen almost laughed. "Michael isn't the violent sort. I promise."

"I'll call you tomorrow."

Cathleen smiled, pleased even in the midst of the emotional chaos. "Yes, please."

He winked and followed the others into the night. Cathleen squeezed her sister and opened her arms. Lynette stepped back, wiping at her teary cheeks with her hands. "Why don't you go to my bedroom?" Cathleen asked gently. "There's a box of tissues on the vanity. I'll be there in a minute, and we can talk."

Lynette sniffled and obeyed, casting a fulminating glance at her husband. Cathleen was left alone with Michael.

"Cathy, what's going on?" he asked in an anguished voice, skirting the couch and striding toward her.

"I'm sure you know as much or more than I do, at this point. Lynette hasn't confided in me. What happened?"

"I don't know!" He threw up his hands in a helpless gesture. "I came home from work and found a note in our bedroom. It said that Lynette had decided to go home, our marriage was past repair and she was going to file for divorce. I was stunned! So I followed her to find out what was going on." He shook his head. "Everything was fine until today. She went to New York for a week to see the plays and shop for a dress for the Swan Ball. I couldn't go with her because we had an unexpected problem at the office. I was the only one with enough authority to handle it. Lynette didn't get angry, though. She just shrugged and said okay. I told her to go without me, because I knew she'd love it. That was the end of it. Or at least I thought it was. Today, when I read the note, the New York trip was the only thing I could think of that would have made her mad. She won't talk to me, Cathleen. She refuses to explain why she left. All she'll say is that it's just everything. What the hell does that mean? Just everything!"

"I don't know." Cathleen touched Michael's arm. He had been obtuse to believe that Lynette wouldn't mind going to New York by herself. However, Cathleen liked Michael and knew he wouldn't have intentionally hurt Lynette. She was inclined to suspect that Lynette's reasons for leaving her husband were relatively trivial and could be resolved to everyone's satisfaction.

"I'll talk to her. Lynette tells me everything eventually. Once she's gotten it off her chest, you two will be able to work it out. I'll do everything I can to help."

"Thank you." Michael clasped her hand fervently between his. "Cathy, you're a lifesaver. Thank heavens you're here to help Lynette. I know she won't go off and do something crazy while you're with her."

His distrust of Lynette's actions nettled, but Cathleen managed a smile. After all, Lynette's upbringing must seem bizarre to a man who belonged to one of Nashville's oldest, most staid families. Cathleen had to admit that there were times when Lynette was anything but steady and commonsensical. "Why don't you go home and let me talk to Lynette? There's no point in pursuing it tonight. You'd get into another wrangle. A night away from each other—maybe even a few days—would do you good."

"You're probably right. I'm exhausted, and I have to be in the office early tomorrow morning. Let me know what you find out."

"I'll call you," Cathleen hedged, carefully avoiding a promise to reveal her sister's secrets. Michael might be a nice man, but she wasn't about to betray Lynette's confidence.

He shook her hand again and said good-night. Cathleen followed him to the front door and let him out, then locked it behind him. For a moment she leaned against the closed door, dreamily thinking of Casey and the afternoon they'd shared. Finally she pushed herself away from the door and shook her head as if to clear it. She drew a deep breath and started down the hall to Lynette.

For the first few minutes after Cathleen joined Lynette, her sister could do nothing but cry. Cathleen sat down beside her on the bed and held her, rocking her and murmuring soothing sounds. Finally Lynette drew a long, shuddering breath and ground to a halt. She straightened and grabbed a handful of tissues to wipe away her tears. "I'm sorry. Wasn't that awful? I didn't mean to bring this mess into your house. I never dreamed that Michael would pursue me. When you weren't here I called Mother to cry on her shoulder a little, but she decided to come comfort me! I wouldn't have called her if I'd thought she'd do that."

"I'm sorry I wasn't here."

"Don't be. Despite all the growling and snapping going on, I saw who you were with. Why didn't you tell me you had something going with Casey? I think he's yummy."

"I don't know whether we 'have something going.' Besides, we're supposed to be discussing your marital crisis, not my love life."

"I'm sure your love life is more interesting than my marriage," Lynette retorted dryly.

"Michael told me he didn't go to New York with you."

"Oh, that." She waved it away. "It's the tip of the iceberg. Don't get your hopes up. It isn't a little tiff over one missed vacation. Michael and I are through. I'm seeing a lawyer tomorrow about a divorce."

"But why? Honey, what happened?"

"Nothing, really. That's part of the problem. I—oh, hell, I'm sick of it all. I can't take being a Stokes. I don't belong in their family, and they let me know it at every opportunity. I'm Dusty Richards and Stella Farrow's kid. No matter how much money my parents made, or how many platinum records are on their walls, Dusty and Stella will never be anything but country to Mike's parents. Neither will I."

"But you've always known that they were snobs," Cathleen pointed out. "It must be more than that."

"I'm going crazy!" Lynette jumped to her feet and began to pace. "I'm so tired of the whole life. Next month's the Swan Ball. Last month it was the Steeple-chase. They think those two things are all there is! What's the big deal about dressing up in an eight-hundred-dollar sundress, heels and a southern belle hat to traipse through Percy Warner Park? It's ridiculous!"

A giggle escaped Cathleen. "I agree. But you used to think it was fun."

"Used to—those are the operative words. After a few years it's pretty senseless. When I married Michael, I thought I'd be happy if I could be Mrs. Michael D. Stokes,

III. All my problems would be solved. I'd be loved and cherished, pampered. I'd really *belong*. I wanted to wallow in family tradition and pride. The sanity, the sameness, even the staidness was appealing. Michael's family was everything ours wasn't. No fights, no drinking binges, no crazy emotional outbursts, no strangers wandering in and out of the house at all hours of the day or night. Nobody gone on tour for two months, no being mobbed for autographs. You know what I mean."

"Yeah, I know."

"I couldn't think of anything more stable than entrenched society. But I found out that being with them doesn't change *me!* I'm still Lynette Richards, the baby 'Country Lullaby' was written for. That whole crazy life is part of me. I'm bored, Cathleen. Bored right down to my toes."

"Have you told Michael?"

"No. He wouldn't understand. Only you have any idea what I'm talking about. Michael can't conceive of his mother bursting into his bedroom at four o'clock in the morning, home from a tour and carrying cherry ice cream cones. Remember that?" Cathleen nodded. "He has even less idea what it's like to hear your parents screaming insults and curses at each other, or to see your father's hand spurting blood because he crashed it into a table of glassware."

"Not many people do."

"Probably not. But it makes it hard for Michael and me to understand each other. I can't imagine his background, and he can't imagine mine. Worse, he expects me to act as if I had grown up as he did, to have the same interests and knowledge and feelings. I can't. I make him mad, and he bores me to tears."

"Lynette, I had no idea. . . ."

"I'm not saying we fought, or that he doesn't love me. He does, in his own way. He's considerate. He dutifully remembers my birthday and our anniversary and gives me lovely, expensive gifts—ordered over the phone from the jewelers. But he doesn't gaze at me like Dusty would at

Stella when she came into the room. We don't go skinny dipping in the middle of the night. I never feel the way Stella looked when they made up after a fight."

A few weeks ago Cathleen wouldn't have understood Lynette's yearning. But after this afternoon with Casey, she knew exactly what had brought the rapturous peace to Stella's face—and she knew how much her sister was missing. "Oh, honey, I'm so sorry."

Lynette stared at her intently. "Do you know? Is that what you feel with Casey?" Cathleen nodded, pink tinging her cheeks. "I think that's what it's all about, really. Not security or a good home or companionship. That spark is the important thing."

"Even when it means fights, betrayals and heart-breaks?"

"Maybe it's worth it." Lynette hesitated. "Cathy, remember when you came by to tell me about Dusty's chance at Sunburst?"

"Yes. You hinted that your marriage was having problems."

"That day I started to tell you something, but I didn't have the nerve. You said you wouldn't hate me no matter what I'd done."

"Of course I wouldn't."

"I . . . I cheated on Michael."

"You—you mean you're in love with someone else?"

Lynette laughed harshly. "Love? I don't think love had anything to do with it. I mean I've been sleeping around. There isn't just one man who's stolen me from Michael. There have been several. Close your mouth, Cathleen; the flies'll get in."

"But, why? I mean, I can understand falling in love with someone else, but . . ."

"Well, it wasn't because of my great sexual appetite, I can tell you that! I kept hoping I'd find what I wanted. I'd dream that every man would be the one who'd make me feel the way Stella and Dusty did. It never happened."

"Maybe it was because you didn't love any of them."

"You're hopelessly naive."

"You're the one who didn't find it, aren't you?" Cathleen shot back.

Lynette's eyes were suddenly dark and empty. "No, I didn't."

"I'm sorry. That was a bitchy thing to say. But I don't think that's the way to find what you want."

Lynette sighed. "I guess not. It'd give me a rush, you know, at first. Then I realized that what I enjoyed was walking into a singles bar and seeing the heads turn toward me, hearing the compliments, having men cluster around me. I felt beautiful and desired, which I didn't feel with Michael. But it wasn't enough. It faded and became ordinary. The men weren't special. I didn't feel glorious or fantastically feminine in bed. I felt as little as I did with Michael. If anything, I was stiffer and more awkward. Maybe I'm incapable of emotion or enjoying sex. What if all those years with our parents drained it out of me?" Her voice dropped to a whisper. "What if I'm frigid?"

"Don't be silly. You're not. There's no reason why you should feel sexual fulfillment with a total stranger."

"I didn't with Mike, either."

"What does that prove, except that you're incompatible? Did you ever feel anything for him?"

"When we were first dating, there was a kind of excitement which I assumed was sexual. Now I think it was just the rush I told you about—the glamour of Michael Stokes loving me, chasing me, telling me I was beautiful. It vanished quickly. I haven't been desperately unhappy. There were no fights, no ugly scenes, no accusations or retaliations. But I'm not happy, or even content. I don't love him."

Cathleen sighed. She felt incapable of coping with this. Why didn't anyone in her family have normal problems, like cars that needed repairing, or children who wouldn't behave? With the Richardses it was infidelity or addiction or complete financial ruin.

"Do you hate me now?" Lynette asked in a small voice, casting a glance at her sister through her eyelashes.

"Silly. Of course not. I told you before, whatever you've

done won't change my love for you. I hate to think of you being unhappy or feeling driven to pick up men in bars, but I don't hate you for it."

"Oh, Cathleen, thank heavens for you," Lynette cried, holding out her arms. Cathleen embraced Lynette tightly, patting her on the back.

"Tell you what. Why don't we go to bed and let everything rest? Maybe tomorrow things won't seem the same. How does that sound?"

"Wonderful. I haven't slept well lately."

They went through much-shortened nightly routines and crawled into the twin beds they had slept in as teenagers. For each of them there was something warm and homey about looking across the space separating the beds and knowing that the other one was there. It had been a long time since they had done so. "Doesn't it seem odd," Lynette asked meditatively, "that I feel closest to you and know you're the only one I can depend on? Is that the way you feel?"

"Yes." Cathleen didn't add that she hadn't always felt that she could depend on anyone, even Lynette.

"It seems like that should be how we feel about our parents."

"Our parents weren't typical."

Lynette laughed. "I think you could safely say that."

"Good-night."

"Good-night. I'm glad you were here."

The sharp peal of the phone pierced Cathleen's sleep. She fumbled for the receiver. "Hello?"

"Good morning, darlin'. Did you sleep well?"

"Casey." It was nice to be awakened by his voice.

"The same," he admitted. "Did 'the honeymooners' ever leave last night?"

She giggled. "Michael left, but not Lynette. She spent the night here." Cathleen glanced across at the opposite bed. The rumpled sheets were thrown aside. Lynette was already up.

"Is it a permanent split, or temporary?"

Cathleen sighed and shoved her tangled hair back from her face. "Permanent, according to Lynette. She may change her mind, but when we talked last night she was adamant that it was over."

"Sorry."

"I guess it's hard to make a marriage work, what with the model Lynette had."

"I believe in free will, personally."

"What's that supposed to mean?"

"We're in charge of our own destinies. Your parents may sidetrack you, but you can get where you want under your own steam."

"Is this a philosophical discussion or a railroad song?"

"Don't get smart, or I won't ask you to spend the day with me."

"Who said I'd come if you asked?"

"Would you?"

"Yes." She supposed it would be more sisterly to remain with Lynette and listen to a rehash of her marital problems. But she'd already sacrificed last night for Lynette. "Are you going to ask?"

"Yes. I'll be there in an hour to pick you up. See you then."

"Okay. Good-bye."

"Bye."

Cathleen jumped out of bed, suddenly full of energy. She put on a robe and crossed the hall to the bathroom. It was steamed over from Lynette's recent bath, but Cathleen scarcely noticed the heat and moisture. She peeled off her robe and nightgown and stepped into the shower. She burst into song as she lathered soap over her body, not even noticing that she was singing one of her mother's hits. "I'm just a calico woman, a country wife." She belted out the lyrics of rural love and it's steadfastness, adding flourishes the song had never before possessed.

There was a loud knock at the bathroom door and Lynette's voice called, "Auditions are at four, lady."

Cathleen laughed. Lynette sounded in a better humor this morning. Good. She wouldn't feel so guilty about spending the day with Casey. Cathleen finished her shower and returned to her room to dress and dry her hair. Lynette was lounging on one of the beds. She indicated a steaming mug atop the dresser. "I thought you might like a cup of coffee."

"Thank you." Cathleen sipped the hot liquid. "Mmm. Delicious. Here's a question: Why are you and I good cooks? I thought that was something you learned from your mother who learned it from her mother, etcetera, etcetera."

"There is such a thing as survival. If your mother can't toast bread without burning it, you either learn to cook or starve."

"Remember the chocolate mousse you made when you were a kid?" Cathleen asked, grinning.

Lynette groaned. "You'll never let me live that one down, will you?"

They teased and laughed while Cathleen got ready for her date with Casey. Lynette offered to do Cathleen's hair. She plaited two tiny braids and pulled them back to the crown of Cathleen's head, anchoring them with a small, ribbon-covered barrette. It was as if they were teenagers again, giggling, gossiping and trying out styles on each other's hair. Cathleen avoided any discussion of Lynette's marriage. She wasn't about to spoil her sister's happy mood. Cathleen liked Michael, but family came first. If Lynette was happier without him, Cathleen wouldn't try to change her sister's mind.

They had a quick breakfast of cereal and milk, finishing it off with another cup of coffee. Lynette opened one of Cathleen's cookbooks and mused over what she would cook for dinner. Cathleen watched her idly, her mind on Casey. He should be here in a few minutes. At that moment she heard a car stop in the driveway, and she rushed to open the kitchen door. Casey was sliding out of his car. He looked up and grinned when he saw her. Cathleen ran lightly down the steps and across the driveway to him. He caught her, lifting her into his kiss. Casey dazzled her senses, flooding her with sensations. She formed no coherent thoughts, but was intensely, primitively aware of the warmth of his arms closing around her, the strength of his muscles, the spicy scent of cologne and flesh mingling, the soft brush of his hair against her hand.

Their kiss was a coming home, a reestablishment of their relationship before Lynette's call for help. Casey left no doubt as to what he had in mind for the day at his farm. When he finally released her, slipping her body down the length of his, Cathleen's breathing was unsteady and Casey's eyes were lit with an unholy gleam.

"You want to come in for a cup of coffee?" Cathleen asked, suddenly awkward.

He hesitated, then shrugged. "Why not?"

They strolled into the kitchen hand in hand. Lynette glanced up from her cookbook and flashed Casey a smile. "Hello, Casey."

"Lynette."

"Sorry for the scene last night."

He smiled again. "No problem. I've seen worse."

For the first time that morning Cathleen noticed how pretty Lynette looked. Her crying the night before hadn't turned her eyes red-rimmed and puffy. She was dressed in a pale golden brown slacks set that complemented her shiny chestnut hair and hazel eyes. Looking at her, an unaccustomed envy shot through Cathleen. She had asked Casey the day before if he had been searching for her mother in her. Had he told her the truth when he'd said no? Cathleen's heart sank to her stomach. Lynette resembled Stella very much.

Chapter 11

CATHLEEN STOOD FROZEN INTO SILENCE AS LYNETTE INVITED Casey to sit down for a cup of coffee. Casey shot a glance at Cathleen, then agreed and slid into one of the kitchen chairs. Lynette cast Casey a glance from beneath her golden lashes and smiled, pouring him a cup of coffee from the pot. Cathleen clenched her hands and sat down. Lynette was teasing her by half flirting with Casey, not turning on the full seductive power she was capable of, but smiling invitingly and tossing back challenging remarks to him.

Don't, Lynette, please don't, Cathleen prayed inside. Her sister wasn't trying to take Casey away. She was merely playing, having fun, and had no intention of hurting Cathleen, because she was unaware of Casey's past love for their mother. She didn't know that Cathleen was afraid that he was interested in her largely because she was Stella's daughter, nor would Lynette realize how likely he was to fall for *her*.

Misery seeped through Cathleen. Without knowing it, Lynette was probably stealing Casey away from her. He and Lynette were chatting now. Cathleen knew that it did her no good to sit there, stiff and silent, but fear immobilized her tongue. Casey shot her a puzzled look now and then. Cathleen wondered where Dusty was, and wished he'd come in to remove Lynette from Casey's presence. But no doubt her father was hiding out to avoid another emotional scene.

There was a cheerful knock on the door, and Cathleen bounded up to answer it. Jack Beaudry stood outside on the stoop, and relief flooded through her. Jack would help her out. She smiled brilliantly. Jack grinned back. "Thought I'd come by and see how you weathered the storm."

Cathleen ushered him inside. He hesitated for an instant when he saw Casey, but went to sit down at the table with the other man and Lynette. "Hey, Casey, nice to see you." He shook Casey's hand and leaned over to peck Lynette on the cheek. "Hi, sweetheart."

"Hi, Jack." Lynette smiled, including him in the conversation. "We were just discussing the Swine Ball." She named a local charitable event which had taken as its theme a humorous spoof of the prestigious social event of Nashville, the Swan Ball. Lynette sparkled at Jack, and his kind brown eyes flickered from Lynette to Casey.

"I figured you wouldn't know about something like that, Lyn," Jack remarked. "Being so society and all."

"Ha. I've given it up. I didn't fit. Here is where I belong."

"In the kitchen?" he queried. "You mean you can't run over to the studio with me? I'm recording this afternoon. I thought you might enjoy seeing the old stomping grounds."

Lynette jumped up from her chair with a little shriek. "Are you kidding? I'd love it. I haven't been inside Sunburst in years. Let me put on my sandals."

She rushed to Cathleen's room, and Cathleen shot Jack a grateful glance. He responded with a wink. Casey watched the exchange, his hand arrested in midair.

"You gonna drink that coffee, Casey, or study it?" Jack asked casually.

Casey set the cup back on the table, not noticing the hot liquid that splashed over the side and landed on his fingers. He gave Jack a long, hard stare which Jack returned with a beatifically innocent face.

When Lynette returned to the kitchen Jack unwound his lanky frame from the chair and opened the side door. "See you folks later," he threw back as he followed Lynette out.

"Yeah, bye!" Lynette called. "You all have a good time."

As soon as they heard the sound of the car engine, Casey grabbed Cathleen's hand. His fingers bit into her flesh, startling her. "Let's get out of here before somebody else decides to come calling," he growled, jerking her to her feet.

"Ouch!" Cathleen exclaimed. "You're hurting me! What do you think you're doing?"

"Sorry." He seemed more abstracted than remorseful. "Are you coming or not?"

"Yes, of course I am."

Tears stung her eyes at his words. His mind was somewhere else, not on her. She wondered if he were thinking about Lynette. His last exchanges with Jack had sounded jealous. It seemed crazy that he could have fallen so quickly for Lynette, but that was the way it looked. Cathleen trailed after Casey, crossing the driveway to his car. He opened the driver's door to let Cathleen slide through. She scooted across the seat to the opposite side. The leather seats were hot from the sun and stung her bare legs below the hem of her shorts. Casey jumped in after her, his jaw set, and turned on the ignition with an impatient flick of his wrist.

For a moment he simply sat, staring at the steering wheel. Then he swiveled to face her, his brows drawn together in a frown. "What the hell is going on? First you act like everything's the same, and you're real happy to see me. Then all of a sudden you stiffen up like a mummy and leave me to make small talk to your sister. If I hadn't seen you, I wouldn't have known you were in the room."

"I had nothing to say."

"Then why did you want to stay and talk?"

"Me? I wasn't the one talking," Cathleen denied heatedly.

"No. I was the one who had to do it. But you were the one who wanted to stay."

"I didn't."

"For heaven's sake, you asked me inside and sat down at the table. What else does that mean?"

"You seemed to enjoy chatting with Lynette."

He rolled his eyes. "Yeah, more than I liked 'chatting' with Jack Beaudry. Why the hell does he hang around your house all the time?"

"He's a friend. Why shouldn't he be there? He's been Dusty's friend for years and years."

Casey made a rude sound of disbelief. "I didn't see Dusty there, just Jack. What was all that eyeing and goggling between you two?"

"All that *what?*" Cathleen stared, caught between anger and laughter.

"Come on, Cath, you know what I mean. Is Jack after you? He's old enough to be your father."

"That's sort of what he is to me. More of an uncle, really."

"Uh-huh. 'Friends of Dusty's' and 'uncles' don't practically live at your house. They don't bring you gifts and—"

"Jack doesn't bring me gifts!" Cathleen interrupted hotly.

"*And . . .*" Casey plowed on, disregarding her interjection, "they sure as hell don't look poleaxed when you walk in the door with another man."

"What are you talking about?"

"I'm talking about the fact that Jack Beaudry is in love with you."

"You've got to be joking!"

"I'm not. Last night, when you and I came in, his mouth fell open a foot."

"He was surprised. He knows how I felt about you in the past."

"No. He knew we'd been making love. Any fool would have realized it, seeing us."

"I'm still a little girl to him. Naturally he was surprised. But it doesn't mean he's in love with me. That's the most ridiculous thing I've ever heard. I've known Jack since I was a kid."

"You've known me a long time, too. But I noticed real quick that you'd grown up. Jack isn't blind, Cathy."

"You're crazy. Why are you talking like this?"

"Because I'm jealous, damn it! I don't care if Jack Beaudry's in love with you. It just shows he's got good sense. What bothers me is how you feel about him."

"Jack?" Cathleen stared. "Jack! I told you, he's like an uncle to me! I'm not in love with him. I'd never—this is the most insane conversation."

"What were those little looks between you two this morning, like you were conspiring?"

Cathleen sighed. "Jack understood the situation. He could tell that Lynette was flirting and I was worried, so he took her away. He was doing me a favor, so I smiled at him to let him know I appreciated it. He just acknowledged it."

"Lynette was flirting with me?" Now Casey was the one to stare. "Where'd you pick that up?"

"I was there," she retorted with asperity. "I'm not blind, either, Casey. Nor am I nearly as stupid as you seem to think."

Suddenly Casey began to chuckle. Cathleen glared, and he laughed harder. "Oh, Cath, you and I are classics. You were jealous because Lynette was talking to me, and I was steamed because you were making signals at Jack."

Cathleen thrust out her jaw, then relaxed into laughter. "Were you actually jealous of Jack?"

"Yes." Casey's face turned serious, and his blue eyes clouded. "You're so fond of him. I thought you were turning to him for something and wouldn't even talk to me. I felt . . . cut out. Then you got in my car and slid as

far away as you could. I didn't know what to think." He
reached out a hand to her, and after a second's hesitation
Cathleen took it and slid back across the seat to nestle
beside him. "Why did it bother you for Lynette to talk to
me? She's always flirtatious, isn't she? I remember her
that way."

"Yes. Flirting's as natural to her as breathing. She's like
Stella in that." Cathleen hesitated, and Casey's frown
cleared.

"Oh, wait a minute. I think I understand. Lynette
resembles Stella. And you think I'm searching for a Stella
substitute, don't you?"

Cathleen nodded, her head lowered, not daring to meet
his eyes. What if his expression revealed that she was right
in her suspicions? Casey sighed. He raised her hand to his
lips, kissing the knuckle of each finger with great care and
tenderness.

"What will it take to convince you that I'm no longer in
love with your mother?" he asked softly. "Baby, I'm not
sure I ever was, not really. Stella dazzled me. Being in love
with her was like a sad country song. She was beyond my
reach, the wife of the man who'd done more for me than
anyone else in my life. Romantic, huh? It was a nice ache
in my heart that didn't keep me from enjoying the charms
of other women. But it wasn't a stabbing pain in my gut
from wanting and not having her. I didn't want to punch
Dusty out for sleeping with her the way I wanted to pop
Jack just for looking at you. My arms didn't feel empty like
they did last night without you."

Cathleen raised her eyes cautiously. "Is that really the
way you feel about me?"

"Oh, Cathy," he breathed and leaned down, his lips
meeting hers with heat and longing. He didn't touch her.
Their only connection was their mouths, and his wooed
hers eloquently. Their tongues found each other, tangled,
then unwound. Still he didn't touch her. Cathleen strained
upward, her eager mouth inviting further advances, and
Casey's breath became harsh and irregular. He pulled
away. "Let's go home."

"All right." Cathleen smiled, feeling almost unbearably alive and feverish.

Casey sped out to his farm, Cathleen snuggled contentedly against his side. He put one arm around her and guided the car with the other, occasionally tapping out a rhythm on the steering wheel with his fingers. Now and then he bent to brush his lips against her hair. "Mmm, you smell nice," he commented. A few minutes later, as she idly twined the exposed hairs on his legs around her fingers, he growled, "You better stop that, or I may have to stop the car right here."

"What?" She raised her head to meet his glittering gaze, and a deep flush stained her cheeks. "I'm sorry."

"Don't be." He smiled. "When we get home, you can do anything you like."

They turned into his road, and he pushed the button on the remote-control unit to open the tall gates. Excitement rose in Cathleen as the car bowled along the asphalt road toward the sprawling house. "Is your housekeeper here today?"

"Yeah, but she'll stay out of our way. She's very discreet."

"You mean she won't pop into your bedroom to announce lunch?"

He chuckled. "Not if she likes her job." Casey stopped in front of the house and cut off the engine. He turned toward her. "Now, do you have any more confusion about whether I like you or your mother or Lynette?"

"No."

"Good." He kissed her lightly. "Let's go inside. I want to show you something I've been thinking about all night."

His grin was wicked, but Cathleen didn't feel a moment's hesitation. She followed him out of the car and through the large front door of his house. A petite black woman was in the living room dusting furniture, and Casey introduced her to Cathleen. Her name was Susan Andrews, and she greeted Cathleen with solemn formality before she turned toward Casey. "Would you like something to drink or eat, Mr. Casey?"

Casey chewed at his lower lip. "Yeah. How about lemonade and sandwiches. Out on the patio." His decision surprised Cathleen until he added, "In about an hour and a half. Cathleen and I will be . . . uh . . . practicing till then."

Mrs. Andrews nodded her compliance, and Casey took off down the hall at a brisk walk, pulling Cathleen after him. He ducked inside the bedroom and closed the door, pulling Cathleen into his arms.

"Practicing?" she teased. "You mean we didn't get it right before?"

He grinned. "You're a witch. That's the first time I've ever been embarrassed with Mrs. Andrews about having a woman with me." His hands roamed down her back and over the firm mounds of her hips. He pressed her against him so that she felt his rising hunger, and instinctively Cathleen rubbed her lower body against his. Casey swallowed and buried his face in her neck, mumbling inarticulate words of desire.

"Love me," Cathleen whispered, her voice husky. "Love me, Casey."

Casey carried her to his wide bed and laid her on it with infinite care. Without taking his eyes from her, he stripped off his clothes. He reached down to undress her, and Cathleen watched the bunching of his muscles as his fingers worked at freeing her from her outfit. The heat of desire rose in his throat and face as her breasts tumbled free of her bra, but he waited until she was completely naked before he stretched out beside her and began to explore the riches of her body. Slowly, carefully, he learned her secrets, finding her most sensitive spots, touching her everywhere and in every way his fancy took him, until finally they were both so lost in the swirl of desire that neither could hold back any longer.

Again he came into her, their bodies fitting together so perfectly that it seemed almost miraculous. Soon Cathleen lost all sense of time and reality. She was no longer one whole person, but part of a single entity that was her and Casey combined. It was a wild, soaring sensation, a freedom beyond anything she had ever felt, as if she had been released from the past and herself. She wanted it to go on forever, yet at the same time she was aware of such an urgency growing within her that she groaned with longing to reach satisfaction. At last she was thrown into a realm of light and color, indescribably beautiful, and for one brief instant of time nothing existed but her and Casey pressed together in perfect union.

Their afternoon was slow and leisurely, neither of them wanting to rush. For a long time they lay languidly in bed, Casey's arm around Cathleen and her head resting on his chest. They laughed and talked in soft murmurs, now and then touching each other as if to make sure the other one was real and not about to leave. Finally Cathleen reminded Casey of the lunch that would be served on the patio by Mrs. Andrews, and he agreed that they should dress and leave the inner sanctum of his bedroom. First, though, they took the shower Casey had planned for the previous evening and were soon so absorbed in the delightful feel of slick, soapy skin that they returned to bed instead of the patio.

When they emerged from the house, glowing and rosy, and took their seats at an umbrella-sheltered table, they found the fruit salad and crustless sandwiches wilted and their drinks lukewarm and watery. It didn't seem to matter, though. They grinned, eyes lighting with amusement. Cathleen hardly tasted the food, anyway. For once she had no interest in eating. No other pleasure could compare to sitting with Casey, warm and sated from his lovemaking.

Afterwards they retired to his studio to choose a song for Dusty's benefit banquet. At first they tinkered with "Heart, Home and World," a bouncy tune that had been one of Dusty and Stella's most popular duets. Its lyrics were simple and direct, and the melody was toe tapping. But after singing it through a couple of times, they drifted into a song Casey had written for Dusty and Stella, "Come Around." It wasn't the merry celebration of love that

"Heart" was, but an aching ballad of a broken love affair. It told of a love too wild to last, of passion and attachment that couldn't withstand the rigors of reality. Tears came into Cathleen's eyes as she sang it. How apropos it was of her parents' love.

"That's it," Casey announced when they finished. "Go with the song you feel. Let's do 'Come Around.'"

They spent the next few hours on the arrangement, forgetting about time as they worked on the music. They added variations to the chorus which would let loose the full range of Cathleen's voice. As Casey sang the words, she soared up and down around him, joining in on some lines, on others hitting key phrases and winding them in and out around Casey's words. Even without amplification, their voices had a richness and power that Stella and Dusty hadn't possessed, and they used these to create a different texture and pattern for the song.

When they stopped, they were surprised to see that it was dark outside. Casey swung around to the clock. It was past midnight. "Don't tell me I'll have to drive you home again," Casey threatened.

"No," Cathleen replied softly, her eyes soft and shining. "I hadn't planned on going home tonight—that is, if you want me to stay."

"You know that's what I want." His voice was gruff with repressed emotion. He strode toward her rapidly. His eyes bored into her, only inches away, burning with desire and promise. "Tonight and every night."

The following weeks were the happiest of Cathleen's life. As Casey had predicted, Sunburst released Cathleen and Dusty's cut of "Dreamer" as the first single, and it was quickly a success. They made a few appearances on local television and radio shows, and Cathleen was surprised to find that she felt little nervousness in front of the camera or microphone. Eddy Lambert had finalized their month-long tour, and Cathleen spent many afternoons rehearsing the show with Dusty and the band, or working with Dusty and the musical director on the arrangements. Also, she had to return to Liz Chase's several times for fittings on her costumes.

Though she was busy with the business of releasing a record and going on tour, she had free time to spend with Casey, and he seemed happy to consume it. Cathleen experienced pangs of guilt at leaving Lynette alone so often, but Jack frequently took Lynette out of the house. Lynette appeared to be happy, despite her divorce proceedings, and Cathleen, too joyful herself to initiate a discussion of marital problems, took Lynette's appearance at face value.

Nearly every day Casey drove into town to visit Cathleen, often bringing her back to his farm. When Cathleen suggested driving to the farm herself, instead of having Casey pick her up, he frowned and growled that he didn't trust her beat-up VW to make it to his farm. "I'd worry about you."

"Oh, Casey! I've driven that car for years. It's not in bad condition. It just looks like it's falling apart. Jack Beaudry's kept up the engine."

Casey frowned even more at the mention of Jack, whom he still maintained was secretly in love with Cathleen. "Tell you what, I'll agree if you'll let me buy you a better car."

"No. Absolutely not."

"Why not? It'll be a birthday present. When's your birthday?"

"October, which is several months away. I refuse to take gifts like that from you."

"Why not?"

"Because I won't be one of your . . . your bought women."

Casey glanced around as if searching for such a personage. "One of my whats? I don't buy women."

"I don't want any favors from you. Okay?"

"Damn, you're stubborn. Come on, Cath, it's no big deal. I'm not trying to purchase your virtue or integrity or whatever. It has nothing to do with your sleeping with me. I'd like to buy you something just because I want to."

"No."

Eventually she yielded to his pressure to the extent of trading in her faithful old heap for a small, new foreign car, but she insisted on purchasing it with her own money.

Casey gave her a remote-control unit to his outer gates and a key to his door, but Cathleen never visited him on her own initiative, always waiting for Casey to invite her, which he never failed to do. They spent almost every day together. They rode horses, swam in his pool, relaxed in the sun, rehearsed their song for the banquet and—most of all—made love. Casey couldn't seem to get enough of her, or she of him. They made love in his wide bed and on the couch of his studio, on a blanket under a tree and stretched out in the quiet night on one of the lounge chairs by the pool.

One late afternoon, after Mrs. Andrews had left, they were dreaming up a song together in his studio when the session degenerated into a laughing, loving tussle. Cathleen broke and ran, but Casey caught her beside the pool. They wrestled, laughing and squirming, the sexual excitement rising in them, until they lost their balance and fell, fully clothed, into the water. Thrashing about, still giggling, they made their way to the shallow end of the pool. Cathleen brushed back her wet hair and swept the water from her face. She glanced up at Casey and found his gaze directed to her wet T-shirt. The thin material was almost transparent when wet, and her breasts were plainly visible beneath the shirt. Casey stared at the pink-brown circles of her nipples and the way the wet shirt molded itself to the outlines of her breasts. She was as exposed as if she had been naked, but it was more enticing because of the pretense that she was clothed.

"You're beautiful," Casey whispered huskily, reaching out to grasp her shoulders. Wonderingly his hands slid down her front, caressing her through the material. Her nipples budded beneath his fingers, and he circled them,

watching them thrust against the cloth. His eyes darkened
as he watched, and the lids drooped lower. He bent to take
one nipple in his mouth, sucking the moisture from the
shirt and sending a frenzy of excitement through Cathleen.
Her other breast received the same attention from him,
and by the time he was through Cathleen felt almost too
weak to stand.

Eagerly they stripped off their clothing and tossed it
onto the concrete. Casey lifted Cathleen, his arms tight
beneath her buttocks, and slid into her. Cathleen ran her
fingers over his arms and shoulders, slick with water. She
wrapped her legs around him and lay back, her upper
torso suspended into the water. The darkening sky was
spread above her, limitless yet sheltering. He began to
move within her, and the water rippled around them, so
that the whole world seemed to join in their lovemaking.
Cathleen dug her fingers into his arms, holding on to his
stability in the moving world, and gave herself up to the
sensations he aroused in her. She cried out loud when she
crested on a joyous wave of pleasure, and Casey gripped
her sides, groaning, as he met her in their secret world of
passion.

It was many hours later when Cathleen awoke suddenly.
She lay in Casey's bed, one of his legs thrown familiarly
over her. The intimacy and trust of his position warmed
her inside. She eased out of the bed and strolled to the
window to gaze out, wondering why she had come so
suddenly awake. Leaning against the cool glass, she stared
out at the dark night sky. In the east the horizon was
brushed with light, signaling the coming of dawn. Cathleen's thoughts drifted. Love glowed within her, and she
was lost in a quiet content she had never known. Softly,
without fanfare, she realized that she loved Casey. She
smiled. Funny. Once the idea of falling in love with him
had terrified her. It didn't seem scary now. It was warm
and wonderful and not at all surprising, the most natural
thing in the world.

The stars had vanished from the sky, she noticed, except

for one pale star competing with the growing glow on the horizon. It must be the morning star, Cathleen thought, faintly surprised. She hadn't known there really was a morning star. She had thought it was merely a romantic expression. But the morning star was there before her, plain and real. A song formed in her mind, a mixing of the discovery of love and discovery of the star. The melody was light and airy. Cathleen smiled. She would call it "Morning Star," and it would be her song of love for Casey.

The days hurtled past, and Dusty's banquet was upon them, with the tour looming only a week away. Liz Chase called to say that the costumes were ready on the day of Dusty's banquet, and Cathleen gratefully rushed to her office to get them. She tried each one on for the last time and stared at herself in wonder. Even the black satin jumpsuit she had worried about looked marvelous. The colors and materials were perfect: simple, soft and feminine, without anything overdone or blatant.

She chose a long-sleeved dress with a wide scooped neck for the banquet. It was floor length and simple in design, its beauty relying on the material: a glowing, shiny fabric of pastel stripes—pink, purple and blue. The luscious colors and the slick finish made the dress look as if it were made out of hard candy. A broad pink satin ribbon circled the waist twice and was tied in a jaunty bow. It was a springlike, happy dress, perfect for the celebration of hope that was the theme of Dusty's banquet.

The dinner was held in the large meeting room of a private club. One long wall was a bank of windows overlooking the golf course, shaded by trees and split by a narrow, winding creek. It was an elegant setting for the expensive benefit. Cathleen had rehearsed on the small stage at one end of the room the week before, but then it hadn't appeared so rich and beautiful.

There was no raised table where Dusty would sit, because he had objected violently to being put on display.

Instead he was seated at a large table in front of the platform, his daughters beside him, and Jack and Casey next to them. John Metcalf and his wife sat across the table, exuding dignity and pride. The arrangement left an empty chair, and Cathleen wondered for whom it was reserved.

Her question was answered shortly before the tribute began when Stella Farrow swept in, her ever-present bodyguard trailing along behind her. She strode straight to their table and greeted everyone with a general smile. The men jumped to their feet, chorusing her name. Cathleen stared, unable to utter a word as Stella settled into the empty seat.

"Hello, Dusty," she greeted him in the vibrant voice so familiar to her fans. "Lynette, honey." She hesitated a fraction of a moment, her gaze turning to Cathleen. "Cathleen."

Cathleen returned her greeting with a stiff nod. She felt Casey's gaze on her and knew he disapproved, but she didn't care. He could try all he wanted, but he'd never convince her to like her mother. They were too different, too apart. What was Stella doing here, anyway? Dusty was always quick to forgive, but wasn't this carrying it a bit far?

Cathleen was nervous about performing in front of the gathering, and having Stella at her table curled her stomach into even tighter knots. She picked at the excellent food and spent most of her time studying Stella while pretending not to see her. As usual Stella was dressed in an outfit that would have overpowered anyone else. The skirt was gold satin and slightly full, with a printed silk overblouse above it. The background of the blouse was the same vivid gold, and it was patterned with blue and purple flowers. A purple sash cinched the waist, leaving the overblouse ruffling daintily at her hips. Cathleen knew that she herself would have looked dumpy in that style, but Stella's tall, thin figure could carry it off. Her golden skin and chestnut hair blended beautifully with the gold dress, and her beauty was vivid enough to outdo even the bold, flashy colors. Cathleen knew that Stella was in her late forties now, but she appeared years younger. Her skin was still taut—Cathleen suspected face-lifts—and even the tiny lines around her mouth and eyes merely softened her looks.

Stella glanced up, and their eyes met. Cathleen looked away hastily. For a second she thought that Stella was about to speak to her, but fortunately John Metcalf chose that moment to rise and begin the show. He made a brief, ponderous speech about Sunburst's welcoming Dusty back to the fold. Cathleen shot Casey a speaking look, and he grinned. Metcalf kept the speech mercifully short and turned the show over to the emcee. The program consisted of short spoken tributes to Dusty by various friends and artists, broken up by renditions of his famous songs.

Casey was one of the first on the program. He talked about Dusty's help at the beginning of his career and his gratitude for it. Then he sang "Cell Without Bars." He motioned for Cathleen to join him. She was grateful that she didn't have to speak. Casey introduced her and the song, and the only thing she had to do was smile at the audience. Her nerves were jumping all over the place, and she pulled a complete blank on the words. But as soon as Casey turned to her, the rest of the world fell away. The lyrics of the song poured out of her. She stared straight into Casey's eyes as they sang, and she knew that her love must be shining out for all the world to see.

When they finished, the thunderous applause jerked her back to the present, and she blushed. Casey winked at her and led her from the stage. They were followed by Jack and a number of other people. Then, to Cathleen's surprise, her mother rose from her place at the table and walked to the dais. She stopped in front of the microphone, thoroughly at home before an audience, and began to speak. Her voice was measured and calm, but nothing could change the throaty vibration that marked her as Stella Farrow. "I owe just about everything to Dusty Richards," she began quietly, smiling down at Dusty. "He gave me my career. He gave me love. And, most of all, he gave me my children."

Cathleen rolled her eyes, and Casey tapped her hand warningly. She pulled her hand away and tucked it into her lap. Stella continued to talk for a few minutes, and finished, "It may sound funny to a lot of people, but I believe that you have only one true love in your life. Dusty, you'll always be that to me. Even though we couldn't make it, honey, you know I wish you the best." Tears sparkled on the ends of her lashes as she extended a hand toward Dusty. "Sing one song with me, for old times' sake."

Dusty bit his lip and shook his head ruefully. Cathleen wondered how the words had affected him. If Stella had started up any hope in him again—Cathleen couldn't think of any punishment horrible enough. Dusty pushed back his chair and bounded lightly onto the stage. He joined hands with Stella, and they sang the tearful ballad, "All in the Past." Afterwards Stella left the stage, and Dusty was stranded up there, forced to make a speech thanking everyone. Embarrassed at displaying his feelings before an audience, he stumbled over the words and rushed off the stage as quickly as possible. Dusty was unable to face a crowd without a guitar in his hands.

The applause stormed around him as he sank into his chair. Twice he had to rise and take a bow to his standing ovation. Finally the noise quieted down, and the band on stage began to play. There would be dancing now in the small space to one side of the stage. Everyone began to talk, freed by the general noise. Cathleen rose, excusing herself, and made her way to the powder room. She wondered how soon she could get Casey to leave. She knew that Dusty wouldn't go until the bitter end. Maybe she could get Jack to take her and Lynette home. She simply couldn't face spending the evening at the same table with her mother.

She entered the luxurious lounge and walked to the wall of mirrors. She reapplied her lipstick and combed her hair, aware that she was stalling. The outer door opened, and Cathleen glanced in the mirror to see who had entered. Her eyes widened. It was Stella.

Chapter 12

CATHLEEN QUICKLY RETURNED HER COMB TO HER BAG AND rose. Tucking the bag under her arm, she started to walk past Stella to the door, but Stella reached out a detaining hand. "Wait. I came in here to talk to you."

"About what?" Cathleen forced herself to look the older woman in the eye. She hated talking to Stella. It brought back too much pain, too many memories she'd rather forget. Why was Stella forcing a confrontation? It had been so much easier when Stella avoided her as assiduously as she avoided her mother.

"Us."

"Us?" Cathleen's voice registered her honest surprise. "What do you mean?"

"Cathy, it's not natural for a mother and daughter not to see each other. Not to speak when they're sitting only three feet apart!"

"I'm not as good at pretending as you are. I can't put on a show for the public's sake."

"I'm not talking about a pretense of good will for the public's sake. I want to settle what's between us."

"Settle?" Cathleen hated the way her voice rose, indicative of the emotional turmoil within her. If only she could be as cool and calm as Stella. "How can you 'settle' what you did ten years ago?"

"What happened ten years ago had nothing to do with you and me. It was between Dusty and myself."

"Everything was always between Dusty and you! Lynette and I were a poor third and fourth. Or were we lower than that?"

Stella sighed, her face suddenly older. "You're so bitter."

"Yes, I'm bitter. What did you expect? Do you want to be a mother now? Do you expect me to forget what you did?" Rage flooded through Cathleen, tinging her cheeks pink and turning her stance rigid. "I don't understand what you're doing here tonight. Why are you trying to get back into Dusty's life and mine?"

"I'm not trying to get back into anything. Dusty was my friend before he was my husband. He'll always be my friend."

"That's almost as pretty as what you said on stage, that he's your one true love."

"He is!" Stella snapped, her hazel eyes burning with a golden fire. "There'll never be another man like Dusty, certainly not in my life. I love him. I always have. We simply couldn't live together. There was too much jealousy and anger and betrayal. It's hell to be in love with an addict."

"You forget that I lived with him, too."

"But you didn't love him with the wild, romantic love I did. When I met Dusty, I thought he was the most wonderful, talented man alive. But an alcoholic crushes dreams."

"So can a career."

"Yes. I admit I wasn't a normal wife and mother. I loved singing as much as I loved Dusty. But there was a difference. I couldn't live without singing, and my career never broke my heart."

"Broke your heart?"

"Yes, broke my heart!" Stella answered fiercely. "Did you think the betrayal was all one-sided? When Dusty was on the road without me, he was unfaithful. Surely you aren't naive enough to think that women didn't chase him, or that he was too strong to give in. But it was a lot more than physical infidelity. Every time Dusty took a drink he betrayed me. Me, our marriage, our home, our children— all the things we had together, everything I'd worked for. I left Dusty because I couldn't stand it any longer. I couldn't stay with Dusty and have any respect for either him or myself. But that doesn't mean I didn't love him."

Cathleen stared across the room at the striped Empire-style couch, focusing on it to keep back the tears. "Did you pay for Dusty's stay at the Villa?"

Stella hesitated, then shrugged. "Yes. I wouldn't give Dusty a dime to buy another bottle, but I'd have given any amount of money to cure him."

"Casey told me you did, but I didn't believe him."

"Now you do?"

"Yes, I suppose. You aren't . . . you aren't going to return to Dusty, are you?"

Stella's laugh was brittle. "Lord, no. I'd probably drive him straight back to drinking, and he'd probably drive me to murder. No. I love Dusty. I admire and respect him. But we could never be lovers again."

"Good. Thank you."

"But, Cathy, none of that has anything to do with us. It never did."

"There is no 'us.' I don't know why you keep saying that."

"I'm your mother! Of course, there's an 'us.' I carried you under my heart for nine months—"

"Please, let's not get maudlin. At least you've never been that," Cathleen interrupted, pleased to hear the crispness in her tone. "Why beat a dead horse? We were never close."

"No, I suppose not. You were more like Dusty, closer to him."

"Lynette was 'Mommy's girl' and I was 'Daddy's girl,'" Cathleen acknowledged caustically.

"That doesn't mean I didn't love you, or that Dusty didn't love Lynette."

"Oh, I know Dusty loved Lynette."

"Neither one of us was a particularly good parent," Stella admitted. "Most mothers weren't on tour half the time. Dusty and I weren't good examples of much of anything. But we had lots of happy times, too. Times when we sang together and laughed. Like when we put in the pool. And remember how sweet it was being together again after a tour? Despite the way he acted, you say you don't doubt Dusty's love. Why do you doubt mine?"

"Because you left us!" Cathleen flared. "Dusty didn't. You left us with him, and took the money instead."

Stella gaped. "Is that what you think? What you've held against me for so many years? You think I didn't want you with me, that I let Dusty buy my children from me?"

"Wasn't that what the whole divorce trial was about? Money?"

"Divorce proceedings get tangled. Once you let a lawyer into your split-up, it becomes a fight, and money is the issue. You can't deal with emotions in court, only material things. I admit I wanted my fair share of the money, and I wanted Greenwood. It was Dusty's present to me and named after my biggest song. It was mine. Though Dusty boosted my career at first, I was the one who kept him on top at the end. The last three years we were married, Dusty would have fallen flat on his face if it hadn't been for me. He was drinking a lot more. If you're honest with yourself, you'll remember that."

"I remember it. I remember helping him to bed almost every night."

"Well, you weren't the only one who put him to bed, believe me. I did my share. And I kept him going on tour. I was the one who made sure he appeared at his shows at least halfway sober. I cajoled and screamed and pleaded, whatever it took. I carried him on my popularity. That was

the main reason I felt guilty about leaving him. I knew it
would mean the end of his career as well as his marriage. I
deserved that money. It wasn't a trade-off. It was mine."

"Lynette and I weren't?"

"You two were almost grown. Lynette was going to
begin college the next year, and you were sixteen. I didn't
think you needed a mother like you did when you were
younger. But I knew Dusty needed you. My leaving would
devastate him. I couldn't bear to take everything from
him. So I agreed to give him custody of you and Lynette."

"You deserted us so as not to cause Dusty grief?"

"I did it to soften the blow, yes. Even then I loved him,
and I hated to leave him all alone. I expected you and
Lynette to visit me. I didn't dream it would mean an end to
my relationship with you!"

"I don't believe you," Cathleen said flatly, her eyes
turning hard. "Why didn't you tell me all this at the time?"

"Would you have listened? After I left, you wouldn't
speak to me."

Cathleen shook her head in a small gesture of denial.
Her head was suddenly aching, and she felt sick inside. Grabbing the skirt of her dress, she swept past Stella.
Stella stepped aside, not trying to stop her. Cathleen
hurried out the door and across the hardwood floor, her
heels clattering in time to her jumping nerves. She wanted
to go home. She wanted Casey.

He was standing beside John Metcalf, leaning lazily
against the table. His mobile mouth was turned down in a
grin, and he smoothed the sides of his mustache in a
familiar gesture. When he saw Cathleen, he straightened
and came forward to meet her. "What's the matter?"

"Nothing. I . . . I don't feel well. Would you take me
home?"

"Sure." He wasted no time about hustling her out of the
plush banquet hall and through the lobby. A nice tip sent
the parking valet running for his car, and moments later
Cathleen was safely ensconced in Casey's pale Mercedes.
Casey didn't try to talk, simply held her hand as he drove
to his farm. When they arrived he searched his medicine

cabinet for aspirin for her headache and led her to the couch. "Can you tell me about it?"

Cathleen shook her head. "It's not important."

"Is it about Stella?" She nodded mutely, and he sighed. "Then I suspect it *is* important. Come on, Cath, I want to help you. Talk to me. Let it out."

She related her conversation with Stella, and suddenly she began to cry. Her sobs were fierce, aching shudders. Casey wrapped his arms around her. Amid the sobs the pain and loneliness of her childhood poured out, ending with the final betrayal of Stella's desertion. Casey said nothing, just rocked her, his arms firm and secure around her, one hand thrust into her hair. Finally Cathleen ran out of tears and words and lay quietly against his chest. She felt drained, yet strangely better. Casey carried her down the hall to his bedroom, and Cathleen leaned her head against his chest, content to let him take care of her. It was secure in his arms, like the moment onstage when she had looked into his eyes and her fear had fled. She was at home.

Dusty's and Cathleen's tour was set to begin late the next week. They would cover twenty-six cities in thirty days. Cathleen dreaded the grind of the travel, and her heart ached at the thought of leaving Casey. Though he never spoke of love, Cathleen was certain that she loved him. She hated to be apart from him for even a day, and she didn't know how she could stand a whole month of it. However, it was something she had to do for Dusty, so she gritted her teeth and didn't express her gloomy thoughts.

The bus was to leave early Thursday morning. It would pick Dusty and Cathleen up at their home, so she didn't stay with Casey that night. Instead she cooked a meal for him at his house and then picked at it, her stomach too constricted to accept any food. Later Casey pulled out his guitar. "I've written a song about you."

"Me?" Cathleen was astonished.

"Of course, you. You're about the only thing on my mind lately. You want to hear it?"

"Sure!" Cathleen's eyes shone.

He strummed the opening bars and began. "I've known a lot of women in my time. . . ." The song went on to describe the powerful impact of a certain new lady in his life and her "heartbreak smile," the chief words of the chorus.

By the time he finished, tears glittered dangerously in her eyes. She was barely able to keep from spilling out her love for him. "Heartbreak Smile?" Surprisingly, her voice was calm. "Does that describe me?"

He grinned. "Sure does, lady. Your smile blew me away the first time I saw it. Actually, I wrote this several weeks ago. I just didn't have the nerve to sing it for you."

She smiled at him, glowing, and they kissed. He squeezed her to him tightly for an instant, then set her away. "I better get you home."

He drove her back to Dusty's house, kissed her goodbye, then caught her to him for one last hug, nuzzling her neck. Then he left abruptly. Cathleen wandered into the house, checked that everything was packed and prepared for bed. Lynette came in at about twelve, smiling. Jack had taken her to a play, and she described the comedy to Cathleen until they were both giggling. After they went to bed, excitement and fear kept Cathleen awake most of the night. When her alarm rang at 3:30 she hadn't slept two full consecutive hours. She stumbled out of bed and dressed in jeans and a T-shirt, not bothering with makeup. Across the room Lynette groaned and covered her head with a pillow. After Cathleen had combed her hair, she ventured into the hall. Dusty, usually a late riser, was bustling about. Rick Lewis, the road manager, carried their instruments and luggage to the dark bus looming on the street outside.

"Hi, baby," Dusty greeted her cheerfully. "Ready to go?"

"I guess. Where'd all your good humor come from?"

Dusty chuckled. "First day adrenaline. Don't you remember?"

She nodded, remembering all too well. But when she was a child she hadn't understood the reasons behind the bustle and energy. All she had known were the gray chill of the predawn hours and the disrupted household, as men scurried around loading up the two buses Dusty and Stella had required. She and Lynette had stood close together, warding off the coming loneliness by physical contact, watching the monstrous machines in the circular driveway of Greenwood, their engines idling ominously. The house-keeper or current babysitter had stood behind the girls as though on the alert to pull them back should they rush the bus. Dusty and Stella had hurried back and forth, their faces eager. Cathleen hadn't understood the pull of the coming tour, or the combined fear and excitement that pumped them full of adrenaline. What she had understood was that once again her parents were leaving—and happy to do so.

Even now she shivered, disturbed by the hour and the activity. She thought of Casey asleep in his bed and wished she could run to him. She wanted to curl up in the safety of his arms. That was impossible, of course. She had obligations to fulfill. She couldn't even call him; it would be cruel to wake him in the middle of the night just to tell him that she didn't want to leave.

She watched the men carry her luggage to the bus, making sure nothing was left behind. Lynette gave up the fight to sleep despite the noise and, putting on a robe, joined Cathleen in the kitchen. The instruments and baggage were stored away in the bottom of the bus, and the costumes, carefully protected in long plastic bags, were hung inside, where they would be less likely to wrinkle. When everything was in place and Dusty was already on the bus greeting the other members of the band, Cathleen reluctantly picked up her purse and hugged Lynette good-bye. She was almost to the bus when Lynette stuck her head out the front door and shouted, "Cathleen! Telephone!"

Cathleen ran back, heart pounding, and grabbed the dangling receiver. "Hello?"

"Hello, darlin'. Sorry I'm late. I didn't realize you were leaving this early."

"Oh, Casey, I'm glad you called. I was thinking about you."

"Were you? That's good to hear."

She lingered for a moment as they murmured the sweet things lovers say when faced with separation, trite to anyone who happened to be listening, but infinitely meaningful to themselves. Dusty appeared in the doorway, twitching with impatience. "Come on, Cathy, we've got to go or we won't make it in time. Tell that lazy scoundrel I'll make him come with us next time."

Cathleen made a face at her father, but whispered a loving farewell and hung up. Her spirits were immeasurably higher as she ran out to the bus. Casey had thought enough of her to call before she left, even though it had meant waking up in the middle of the night. Did that mean he would miss her as much as she would miss him? She smiled to herself as she flopped into a seat at the front of the bus. Behind her Dusty sat down to a poker game with three of the musicians. Everyone else had found a spot and arranged themselves as comfortably as possible to sleep. Cathleen took one of the pillows from the overhead rack, settled it in the corner of the double-wide seat and curled up against it. Before they were out of Nashville she was asleep.

She dozed fitfully most of the way to Knoxville, where they stopped for breakfast. A few cups of coffee banished her sleepiness, but left her groggy. When they returned to the bus she tried reading, but found it difficult to do while riding. Joyce Woicek, the girlfriend of Rick, the road manager, joined Cathleen as they rode through the breathtaking scenery of the Blue Ridge Mountains. They chatted in between exclamations of awe at the view. Joyce was the opposite of blond, outgoing Rick. She was a tiny brunette, rather shy and easygoing to the point of laziness. Joyce confided how nice it was to have another woman along besides the groupies some musicians picked up on tour. As they talked Cathleen warmed to her and soon decided that it would have been dismal to have had no companions on this month-long trip except her father, the musicians and an occasional stray girl.

Their conversation passed the time, but the trip to Charlotte, North Carolina, was a long one. By the time they arrived Cathleen was thoroughly tired. They checked into the motel, and afterwards most of the musicians and technicians went to the auditorium to set up the equipment for the show that night. Cathleen seized the opportunity to take a nap. When she awoke she felt rested, and her head was clear for the first time that day. She glanced at her watch and realized that it was less than three hours until showtime. Panic gripped her stomach. The fear she had experienced before Dusty's testimonial banquet was nothing compared to this wrenching terror. She would be facing thousands of people tonight, not just a couple of hundred, and they wouldn't be good-natured peers of Dusty's but men and women who expected professional entertainment. Her hands began to tremble.

Struggling to remain calm, Cathleen undressed and showered, then dried her hair and slipped back into casual clothes. She looked at her watch again and wondered why Dusty hadn't appeared to take her to the auditorium. Moments later her father knocked on the door and whisked her out to a waiting car. They were driven to the auditorium. Dusty held one of her cold hands. They arrived at a barricade of police, and the driver showed his identification. The car was waved on, and the driver zipped around to the back of the large auditorium, where another set of policemen waited at the locked metal doors. Dusty grasped Cathleen's arm, and they ran up a set of stone steps and through the doors held open by the policemen. The guards smiled at them, and Dusty greeted the men as if they were longtime friends.

Inside they strode along a barren concrete hall. People milled about. Some were technicians and musicians whom Cathleen knew, others were people she'd never seen before. All sported laminated cards proclaiming them to be among the privileged set allowed backstage. Rick

Lewis shouted from the other end of the hall and hurried toward them full steam, as usual. A portly man followed in his wake. Rick introduced the man as the manager of the facility. The manager shook Dusty's hand vigorously and gave Cathleen a slight bow. A huge grin split his face as he enthused to Dusty about how long he'd been a fan of his. Dusty charmed him with his usual ease.

"I'd like for you to meet my wife, Elizabeth," the manager concluded, his tone somewhere between a statement and question. "She's a real fan of yours, and I know she'd love to see you in person."

"Sure." Dusty grinned. "Bring her by after the show."

The manager left, and Rick directed them toward their dressing rooms. They were stopped twice by auditorium personnel who had slipped backstage for a glimpse of Dusty and an autograph. One young woman grabbed Cathleen's hand and gushed, "I loved 'Dreamer.' You're the most marvelous singer. Is it true you're seeing C.J. Casey?"

While Cathleen stammered, unprepared, Dusty smoothly turned the girl away and shoved an autograph book into Cathleen's hands. She signed it automatically and slipped away to her dressing room. She closed the door and leaned back against it, sighing. Her first autograph—and her first prying question. Well, not her first, perhaps, but the first one since she had become an adult. It was part of the price of being a public figure, and she knew it better than most. Still, she hadn't been prepared for it, especially with her nerves in the state they were in tonight. Cathleen swallowed hard and drew a couple of deep breaths, firmly fixing her mind on what she must do. Makeup. Her hair. Her dress. If she concentrated on them, the fear wouldn't be able to invade her.

Stage makeup was heavy and dark to counter the washing-out effect of the bright lights. Cathleen wasn't experienced at applying it, but she remembered the many times she had watched her mother put it on backstage at the Grand Ole Opry. During the past few weeks she had practiced several times, using her memories of Stella as a guide and Casey as a judge. First she put on clown's white around her eyes, the upper lids as well as the lower, to make them stand out. Then came the pancake makeup, a shade darker than her skin. She emphasized the color of her eyes with blue shadow, and used eye liner and then mascara to make her lashes look dark and thick. The final touch for her eyes was a tiny red dot at the inner corner. Then rouge for her cheekbones and a light brown triangle below the cheekbone to thin her cheeks. Red lipstick and a gloss to make her lips shine. There was no need to darken her eyebrows; they were already black and well shaped.

She stepped back from the lighted mirror and examined herself critically. She looked like a streetwalker, she decided, and stuck out her tongue at the image. But anything less would make her look sick under the glaring stage lights. She powdered her face with translucent powder to remove the shine and lightly wiped away the excess with a tissue. That called for a touch-up of mascara and lipstick, and she reminded herself to apply the powder before the other two next time.

Next she pulled on her hose and slip, covering them temporarily with an old robe. She brushed her hair and set a wig box on the dressing table, pulling from it the hairpiece so carefully styled by her hairdresser into a coiled knot of curls. After pinning it on the crown of her head, she combed her own hair over the edge until the creation looked like her real hair. With an electric curling iron she created a few casually curling tendrils at the temples. It was an elaborate hairdo, more formal than her own chin-length hair. But the pins dug into her scalp and the hairpiece weighed heavily on her head. She didn't think she would wear it with her less elegant costumes.

She was ready for her dress. Cathleen zipped open the long plastic garment bag and removed the first dress. She had arranged the dresses in the order in which she would wear them. A memory of her mother's dresser popped into her mind. Willamine Reinhart from Hogscald Hollow, Georgia. She was a fat, stern-visaged woman whose clothes were too large even for her, and whose hair was

caught in a bun so tight it should have made her eyes
bulge. Willamine had let no one but herself touch Stella
Farrow's clothes. She packed and unpacked and cleaned
them. She eased them over Stella's high, puffed hairdos
and zipped them up, pinning and tucking to make them fit
exactly right. Also she had arranged Stella's hair with an
artist's hands and fastened her necklaces around the
splendid smooth column of Stella's throat. But Stella had
been wealthy and famous by the time Cathleen came
along. Before that she had done it all herself, just as
Cathleen was doing. Before her career took her far
enough to meet Dusty's eyes, she had even sewn her
costumes. She had also driven herself in a beat-up Ford
from job to audition to radio interview—agent, p.r. man,
costumer and singer all rolled up into one. Cathleen had to
admit that she wouldn't have had Stella's determination or
grit . . . or gall.

Cathleen took the royal blue gown from its hanger,
unfastened the front, and slid her arms into it as she would
a coat. The bodice fastened with hooks and eyes from its
deep V neckline to the waist. The long skirt wrapped
around and a taffeta sash was tied into a huge bow in the
front. Tying the bow just right was difficult, and Cathleen
redid it three times before it looked right. She took three
straight pins from a box in her makeup bag and pinned the
two sides of the skirt together halfway down her thigh to
ensure that the skirt wouldn't flare open too much when
she moved with the music as she sang. Stepping back, she
smoothed the dress and took stock of herself in the mirror.

The dress was stunning on her, which was the reason she
had chosen to wear it that night. The vivid color turned her
eyes into huge orbs of blue. The narrow ruffles around the
neck, hem and up the front of the skirt were soft and
feminine without being fluttery. The deep V neckline and
the split skirt, which would open with her steps to reveal
calves and knees, were sexy without revealing much. Her
waist looked tiny inside the wide sash. Cathleen smiled at
her reflection, pleased even in the midst of her nerves. Liz
had done a beautiful job.

Crossing to the dressing table, she looked at her watch. Eight-thirty. Still thirty minutes until Dusty went on, and she would join him onstage later than that. Cathleen paced, disinclined to sit down for fear of wrinkling her dress. The first act, a local group hired to warm up the audience and absorb the nuisance of latecomers, was going strong. She could hear the vibrations clear back there, though she couldn't understand the words. Cathleen twisted her hands. Perhaps it would be better to wait with Dusty. He'd be reassuring and quell the icy writhing in her stomach.

The music from onstage was louder in the corridor, muffling her footsteps. The next door was open, and Cathleen slipped in. It was a large room and held Dusty and his band members as well as the road manager, his crew and several other men Cathleen didn't recognize. Dusty was chatting to one of the strangers, smoking, arms crossed, looking for all the world like a man with nothing on his mind. But Cathleen knew him well enough to recognize the signs of almost feverish excitement—the occasional twitch of his fingers, the high-wattage smile, the intense blue of his eyes. Dusty was keyed up, and it showed in his heightened personality. No one was more charming, more compelling, than Dusty in the grip of showtime nerves.

"Cathy!" he called, and waved at her to join him. She went reluctantly, wishing she hadn't decided to come in here. She hadn't realized that his dressing room would be filled with people, most of them strangers. When she reached Dusty, he cheerfully introduced her to the man with whom he was conversing. "Cathleen, this is George Haverland. He's a journalist."

"Nice to meet you," Cathleen replied automatically, and smiled, though her insides froze. The media—that must be who the strangers were. Newspapers, TV, radio. Not friends and well-wishers, but people who had come to judge and snoop. It was too much, she thought frantically, to put up a friendly, grinning front for them when she was shaking inside. It was like having to die in public.

Mr. Haverland smiled and supplied the name of the local newspaper he wrote for. "I've listened to 'Dreamer' many times, Miss Richards. I admire your talent."

"Thank you."

"But with parents like yours, what else could I expect?"

Dusty chuckled. "Now, George, you've heard me sing. Don't tell me you think my little girl gets her voice from me. She puts me in the shade."

Haverland joined in his laughter. "I have to admit, she doesn't sound like you. Or look like you, either."

"Thank God," Dusty countered.

Cathleen forced herself to smile until she was sure her cheeks would crack. Haverland went on to discuss Stella Farrow and Cathleen's lack of similarity to her, also. Dusty listened and chatted with great good humor, pointing out the throaty sound of Cathleen's low notes, which was reminiscent of Stella's voice. Cathleen couldn't understand how he did it. She was hardly able to smile and nod politely, let alone chat and joke—and it wasn't the first night of her great comeback tour, as it was for Dusty. Of course, he was accustomed to dealing with the press and experienced at opening nights. Still . . . she marveled at his ability to remain relaxed and jovial.

Haverland hung on, obviously reluctant to end his moment of rubbing elbows with the stars. He finally moved, but only because Rick politely edged him aside so he could introduce a reviewer for one of the television stations. Again they went through the polite motions. Cathleen was trying to think of an excuse to return to her dressing room when the sounds of the band onstage stopped. The crew whisked out to set up the stage for Dusty's band. The media members took last sips of their drinks before they left the backstage area for their choice seats out front. No one wanted to miss Dusty's entrance.

When they had disappeared, Dusty squeezed Cathleen's hand. She was amazed to find his fingers as icy as hers. "It'll be ten minutes. Let's get a breath of air, huh?"

"Okay." He led her down the cement-block corridor to the outer door. A policeman stood on the small porch

beyond the door. He turned with an expression of mild
interest, then smiled broadly. "Mr. Richards!"

"Dusty," her father corrected quickly, the familiar grin
lighting his face.

"Dusty. I'm real proud to meet you. I was disappointed
when I heard you'd arrived before I got here. You know,
I've been a fan of yours for years."

Dusty thanked him and introduced Cathleen. The policeman took her hand with awe. "You're almost as pretty
as your mama," he told her, then looked mortified. "Oh,
excuse me. I'm sorry. I didn't mean that like it sounded."

He was so genuinely embarrassed that Cathleen had to
laugh despite her nervousness. "It's all right. I take after
Dusty, I'm afraid."

"Aren't many as pretty as Stella, anyway," Dusty put in
easily.

Reassured that he hadn't offended them, the man asked
Dusty for an autograph. "I'd say it was for my kids, but I
can't lie. I'm the one who wants it. I've been on duty at
lots of these shows, and I'll tell you, you're the only one
I've wanted to meet."

Dusty obligingly signed a scrap of paper and handed it
back. Cathleen was touched when the policeman offered it
to her. She signed her name and handed back the autograph. Dusty nodded to the policeman and smiled. "Time
to go. Nice to have met you."

They ducked inside, and Dusty heaved a sigh after the
heavy door eased to behind them. "No rest for the wicked,
my mama used to say," he quipped.

"I thought it was 'no rest for the weary.'"

"I told you, Mama came from a long line of hellfire-and-
damnationers." He closed his eyes, resting in the compara-
tive isolation of the dim hall. "Boy, I tell you, honey, this
is a hell of a lot harder to do without a drink. Next time
that shrink asks me why I drink, I'll take him to a show
with me."

Cathleen's hand touched his arm in alarm. "Daddy?"

Dusty opened his eyes and saw her concern. He shook
his head, chuckling mirthlessly. "Don't worry. I haven't

started again. I'll get through this without a drink. It's
just . . . I get so scared, you know, wondering if I'll flop,
or if they'll like me. But on the outside I have to be a
laughing, good old boy for whoever might be around. It's
not a private life. Your only privacy is deep in here." He
touched his forehead. "And that's what the counselors tell
me to let out. They don't understand about protecting
myself from the pulling and poking."

"I couldn't tell you were scared. I thought I was the only
one."

"I don't think there was ever a concert I wasn't scared
of, unless I was drunk."

"Why put yourself through it?"

He raised his eyebrows in surprise. "Why? What else is
there to do? I don't think I could live without it."

"You couldn't live without being scared?"

He frowned at her. "Don't you feel it? The excitement,
the—I don't know how to describe it. I feel alive and . . .
and ready to bust out all over."

"I'm scared and a little eager, but I don't think it's the
same."

"Nope. Probably not. You're like Casey. That boy
always enjoyed it, but he didn't *need* it. You know what I
mean? Your mama needs it even more than I do, but she
doesn't have the fear. She loves it and rushes out all het
up, eager to meet them. There's nothing Stella loves like
an audience."

"It feeds her ego," Cathleen explained caustically.

He shrugged. "You sound like those shrinks at the Villa.
All I know is, an audience gives her something I never
could—or any other man, I guess, considering how many
times she's been married. She doesn't feel whole except
when she's onstage."

"I'm glad you're not like that."

"I'm not any better. I don't ever feel whole, onstage or
off. That's why I used to drink."

The stage manager appeared at the end of the hall and
motioned to Dusty. He waved back. The members of the

band ambled out of the dressing room and toward the stage. Dusty turned to Cathleen. "Coming to watch?"

"Of course."

The sound of applause grew louder as they neared the auditorium. The band filed onto the stage. The stage manager nodded and winked at them, pushing the microphone of his headset out of the way to say, "Good crowd tonight."

Dusty's guitar rested against a stool, and on the seat of the stool lay his white straw cowboy hat. He picked up the guitar and swung the wide woven strap over his head and right arm. The band members were in place now and playing an instrumental. The clapping of the audience grew louder and more restive. Dusty winked at Cathleen and leaned closer so he could be heard above the crowd noise. "Don't worry about your old man. I'm always okay once I get onstage."

"I know. Daddy, I love you."

He smiled and affectionately touched a knuckle to the tip of her nose. "Love you, too, sweetpea." He used the nickname he had given her when she was a child. Dusty settled his hat at just the right angle and waited, poised, judging the audience with his innate sense of showmanship. At precisely the right moment he tensed and strode out into the wild glitter of light.

Chapter 13

Dusty was greeted with a roar. He raised his right hand and grinned at the mass of people before him, though Cathleen knew that the sudden glare of the spotlight made it impossible for him to see the audience at first. But Dusty knew them without seeing them; he felt them with the extra sense of true performers. He loved them, and they returned that love, and for the next hour he would hold the crowd in the palm of his hand.

He wore a purple satin shirt which intensified the color of his eyes, the yoke embroidered with sequins and tiny glass beads that reflected the lights with dazzling effect. The devil-may-care set of his cowboy hat perfected his loose, carefree image. He plugged in his guitar and adjusted it as the audience continued to clap and shout. The band began the opening notes of "Sullivan's Fall," and the noise of the crowd swooped upward, then dropped so the song could be heard. Dusty stepped up to the mike. "It's great to be back in the land of the living," he commented, and the audience erupted again. He began to sing.

192

Cathleen stopped worrying. Dusty would be okay from now on. What he had revealed to her earlier brought a funny ache to her chest, but she pushed it away. Maybe Dusty would never be completely happy. Was anybody? But tonight was his night, and she was determined to feel only pride and joy for him.

Dusty was in his element. He controlled his audience with a master's touch. His concerts were famous for the good show he always put on. The musical director, Sam Goodman, who also played the electric keyboard in the show, had arranged the mix of songs, skillfully blending fast and slow, hard and soft, modern and old, to maintain the audience's interest. The stage manager made sure the lights and special effects, such as firecrackerlike explosions, worked on time and as they were supposed to, adding glitter and excitement to the show. But it was Dusty's charisma that mesmerized the audience and made them his.

He had adjusted easily to the flashier musical and lighting aspects of modern country and western concerts, but he had also retained the easygoing charm which had characterized his previous shows. Now and then he would drop in a humorous comment between songs or stop to chat, as if he and each person in the crowd were personal friends. He made light of his bad years, tossing in jokes about his former drinking habits and even kidding about his emotionally charged marriage to Stella. When he sang he enfolded them in the magic of his songs, making them a part of the fantasies he wove with music and words.

Even Cathleen was drawn under his spell, forgetting her stage fright as she watched him from the wings. Then the band played "Losin' Again," and Cathleen realized with a rush of panic that it was her cue. She would be on next. The notes of the song drifted to a close, and Dusty spoke into the microphone. "You know, a lot of times I lost, but I always had one special fan. She kept me from being a loser. I'm going to bring her out now, and I'd like for you to give a very special welcome to my daughter: Cathleen Richards!"

His words blasted in her ears, and for an instant
Cathleen froze. Luckily instinct took over, and she accepted the microphone the stage manager offered her and
strolled onstage. She had rehearsed her smiling entrance a
hundred times and practiced the retort she would toss
back at Dusty when he spoke to her. Automatically she
did it now, even though her chest was crushed with fear.
As she looked out at the audience, she was thankful that
her eyes were too dazzled by the spotlight to see their
faces. It made them less real, almost as if there weren't
people out there, only she, Dusty and the band, as in
rehearsals.

They sang "Dreamer," and the audience roared approval. Cathleen's blood started flowing again, warming her
hands and feet and bringing color to her face. She drew
strength from Dusty, gazing into his face as she sang and
letting the warmth of his smile encourage her. By the time
the song was over and the crowd rose to their feet,
clapping, she was able to smile and face the people even
though her eyes had adjusted to the light. They were
remote, unreal, yet their applause and patent approval
warmed her. They liked her! She flushed with happiness
and understood why Dusty and Casey enjoyed live performances.

She sang two solos and left the stage to a clamor of
applause and whistles. She floated several inches off the
ground as she watched the remainder of the show from the
wings. The final number was the sad, semislow, "All in
the Past," the song Stella and Dusty had sung together
at the testimonial dinner. It was a wrenching song, and
Dusty had chosen to sing it with Cathleen to end the act.

He called her out again, and this time she moved
forward confidently, buoyed by her earlier success. The
song began slowly, and Cathleen was silent, head bowed,
as Dusty sang the first verse. Dusty sang all the verses, and
on the first few choruses, Cathleen came in a half-beat
behind him, repeating his words in her clear, high voice
with the haunting quality of an echo. The song built in
power, and the chorus was repeated twice at the end. The

first time Cathleen took off on her own in a melodic series of swoops and falls. On the final repetition, father and daughter burst out together and rocketed to the powerful climax.

It left the audience stunned. There was a fragile instant of silence when Cathleen and Dusty stopped. They bowed, breaking the spell, and pandemonium broke loose. They rose from their bow wreathed in smiles. Dusty clasped her hand, and they raised their hands to the audience, drinking in the applause. The people rose to their feet, screaming, whistling, stamping, drumming on the seats in front of them. After several more bows Dusty and Cathleen walked off the stage. Dusty lifted her off the ground and whirled her around. "We did it, honey!" he shouted above the noise. "They loved us."

"Okay, Dusty." The stage manager motioned to them.

They walked back onstage to do their preplanned encore. First they sang a cheerful, bouncing song named "The Happy Train." It was loud and fast, and the excited audience remained on its feet, stomping and clapping in time to the music. Then Cathleen left the stage, and Dusty sang the last planned song, his most popular one of all time, "Blackjack 'n Water." When he finished, the noise reverberated to the top of the cavernous auditorium. With a wave and a grin, he ran offstage. He hugged Cathleen again and vigorously shook hands with the stage manager and Rick Lewis. The noise kept up, and Dusty bounced back onto the stage. His fans knew him. One of Dusty's trademarks was his inability to turn down an audience. He had been known to stay onstage for an hour after his scheduled show had ended, singing encores for an avid crowd. Tonight he managed to limit himself to only five extra songs before he left the stage for good.

After the show the dressing room was a babble of voices. Every member of the crew and the local band joined the band members there. Champagne corks were flying as celebratory drinks were poured, and raucous laughter filled the room. The media returned, as did everyone connected with the show or with enough pull to get invited backstage. Cathleen had no aversion to talking to the press now. Giddy with success and unspent energy, she chatted and laughed, signing autographs and making pleasant small talk with all the people who had wormed their way backstage, bringing along their girlfriends or wives or children. It was a madhouse, but no one seemed to mind.

It was almost two o'clock before the gathering broke up. The crews had long since packed the equipment and loaded it on the bus, along with the costumes, makeup bags and the stacks of T-shirts and memorabilia offered for sale before and after each show. Cathleen followed the others to the bus and collapsed in a seat, once again clad in her simple jeans and shirt. She realized suddenly how tired she was and wondered if she'd be able to stay awake until they reached the hotel. She had been up for almost twenty-four hours now, and the emotional excitement of the show had left her drained.

When they reached the hotel she went straight to her room, although Dusty and several of the others continued their rehash of the night in his room. Cathleen staggered straight to the bathroom to remove her heavy makeup, making a mental note to do that chore immediately after the show from now on. When her face was duly cleaned she shucked off her clothes, threw back the covers and fell into bed. As she was slipping into darkness the shrill ring of the phone sent her shooting out of bed. She grabbed the receiver and whispered, "Yes?"

"Cath, it's me."

"Casey!" Suddenly the weariness left her. "I'm glad you called."

"I don't need to ask how the show went. I can hear it in your voice." He chuckled.

"Ask me anyway."

"Okay. How was the show?"

She babbled about the concert, describing the audience's reactions and her own. She could picture Casey's slow, sexy smile, his eyes lighting with amusement, and it warmed her to think he cared enough to call. Gradually her second wind wore off, and her voice began to slow and slur.

"Darlin', I think you're getting sleepy."

"Mmm-hmm." She had to admit it. Her eyes kept closing.

"I'll let you get some sleep, then. I just wanted to find out how it went and to let you know I missed you."

"I miss you, too." Suddenly she realized how true that was. Cathleen wished he were there beside her, so she could cuddle up to him and go to sleep with her head on his warm shoulder. "I wish you were here."

"Me, too." He hesitated, then his voice came softly across the line. "I love you."

He was gone before she could recover from the shock enough to answer. Casey had said he loved her. Cathleen slipped down in her bed and pulled the sheet up to her chin, pressing her hand against her mouth as if to contain the joy welling up inside her. Casey loved her!

"I love you, too," she whispered to the silent ceiling.

The tour was a continual repetition of the first night, and the different cities and audiences were soon an indistinguishable blur in Cathleen's mind. Each morning they got onto the bus and rode to a new city where they checked into another motel. In the evening they sang before a packed house. Cathleen usually ran too late to eat breakfast before they left and made do with a cinnamon roll and a cup of coffee aboard the bus. Lunch was a sandwich bought somewhere along the road and eaten on the bus to avoid gaping fans. Nerves still attacked her before the show, and she was unable to eat supper, so she grew into the habit of eating a meal after the show, as Dusty did. They frequented the restaurants connected to the motels where they stayed, since they were the most convenient. Often, if the restaurant was crowded, they ordered their food sent to Dusty's room, because Cathleen hated eating under the scrutiny of a roomful of eyes.

Cathleen suspected that she wouldn't have been noticed by herself, but in Dusty's company it was almost impossible to go unrecognized. He had been a flamboyant figure all during his career, and because he made "good press," he had been prominently pictured in newspapers and magazines recently. Plus, there had been a great deal of publicity for this album and tour, including magazine articles and spots on talk shows, so that lately Dusty's face seemed to be everywhere anyone looked. Dusty soaked up the interest and adulation, not seeming to mind if he had to eat his soup cold or his chilled fruit cup warm. Nor did it make him nervous to be on public view. But Cathleen thought with longing of the private dinners she had had with Casey, who did everything possible to protect her from the consequences of his fame.

At first the new experience of singing in front of huge crowds and traveling to new cities held Cathleen's interest. She was thrilled by the deafening applause and caught up in the magic of the show. But the newness soon wore off, and she discovered that the tour was nine-tenths boredom. Traveling in the bus or sitting in motel rooms took up most of her day. She didn't know how to knit or do needlepoint to occupy her hands as she rode, and reading on the bus made her feel nauseous. Dusty was usually involved in a poker game or "picking" with the other band members, and sometimes they engaged in outrageous stunts to break the boredom. But Cathleen had no desire to get involved in any of those things. In fact, as a woman and Dusty's daughter, she was more or less excluded from their activities.

Rick's girlfriend Joyce often joined her to talk, and they became friends. Joyce taught her how to crochet, which helped relieve the boredom, but after a couple of afghans, Cathleen began to wonder what she could possibly do with the products of her new skill. It wasn't long before the essential monotony of the days overcame her interest in chatting with her new friend and trying out different kinds of handwork. In time, even the shows settled into a stultifying sameness. Familiarity eased her preshow jitters, but it also decreased the excitement of the audience's response. One show blended into another, just as the motels did, and after a couple of weeks Cathleen no longer knew what town she was in without asking the road manager.

The brightest spots of the tour were her nightly telephone calls from Casey. Sometimes she was so tired that she almost fell asleep talking to him. Other times she chattered like a magpie, retelling the events of the day with an eagerness that made Casey chuckle. But every night they murmured of their love for each other and the aching hole in their lives where the other one belonged. Often, after she hung up the phone, Cathleen cried herself to sleep.

Two weeks after they left Nashville, they had almost finished their tour of the South and the Eastern Seaboard. They played New Orleans, where they would have one day of rest before continuing to Houston and points west. After the concert, Rick and Joyce joined Dusty and several of the other band members for a night on the town. However, Cathleen, though keyed up, stayed in her room and ordered a tray of food brought up. She didn't want to miss Casey's phone call. It came earlier than usual, and Cathleen pounced on it. "Hello?"

"Hi, love. I was afraid you wouldn't be there yet, but I couldn't wait any longer." Casey's voice came over the phone as clear and alive as if he were in the next room.

"I've been thinking about you all day."

"Me, too. How much longer does this tour last, anyway? I've been taking too many cold showers lately to suit me."

Cathleen chuckled. "Just make sure you keep taking them instead of finding a girl to ease your . . . uh . . . distress."

"Just any girl couldn't do that. Only you."

Cathleen closed her eyes, her insides melting at his husky words. "I miss you."

"You know what I've been thinking about?"

"No, what?"

"How much I'd like to have you lying here beside me right now. I know exactly what you'd have on."

Cathleen's breath caught in her throat. "What?"

"Nothing. No. Maybe a wet T-shirt like the one you wore the day we fell in the pool." Cathleen swallowed and began to twist the telephone cord around her index finger as he talked, hardly aware of how tightly she squeezed her legs together. "Yeah, a wet T-shirt molding to your breasts. I could see the luscious mounds of your breasts, the dark circles of your nipples, the little button centers pushing out the cloth. They'd be hard and pointed, and I'd ache to touch them."

"Casey, you're crazy. Stop it." Her voice was breathless.

"I know. I'll be ready for another cold shower pretty soon. Cath . . ."

"What?"

"Can you see it, too?"

"Yes." Her voice was slightly uneven. "I can imagine you in your bed, naked, looking at me. I feel how tight your chest is, the way your arms bulge when you shift position. The hollow of your throat is deep, and I love to kiss it. I want to bathe it with my tongue."

"Oh, baby. You're better at this game than I am. I may explode."

Cathleen shifted in her bed, trying to find a more comfortable position. Finally she snuggled against her pillow. "Tell me what you would do to me while I'm wearing this wet T-shirt."

He groaned. "You're trying to torture me."

"You started it."

Casey drew in a long breath. "You've got me there. Okay. What I want is to run my hand all over that shirt, feel your skin through the wet cloth. I want to touch your nipples and see them stretch out to me. Then I'd take them in my mouth, and my hand would go down. Your skin is like satin, particularly between your legs. I'd make love to you with my fingers, and then with my tongue, until you begged me to take you."

"And would you do it?" she breathed.

"Yes. But once wouldn't be enough."

"No?"

"Not to show you how much I wanted you. How much I loved you."

Tears sparkled in her eyes. "I wish you were here. I miss you so much. This is crazy. Now I'll never go to sleep tonight."

"What do you have on?"

"Huh? You mean really?"

"Yeah."

"A nightgown."

"Do me a favor. Take it off."

"What? Why?"

"Humor me. I like to imagine you lying in bed naked, with nothing but a sheet against your skin."

"Okay."

"Do it right now. As soon as I hang up."

"I will."

"And think of me while you're lying there."

"Believe me, I won't be able to think of anything else."

"Good. I love you." His voice was a whisper.

"I love you, too."

The phone clicked dead in her ear, and she hung it up. Languidly she rose and stretched, amazed at the sensitivity of her skin. She shrugged off the thin gown. It scraped over her flesh, inflaming her already throbbing nerves. How did Casey manage to have such control over her? She was practically panting for his lovemaking, and he was hundreds of miles away.

She turned out the light and slipped into bed, pulling the sheet up over her. It lay lightly on her skin, faintly abrading the sensitive peaks of her breasts every time she moved. She thought of Casey, pretending it was his hand touching her instead of the sheet, and her heartbeat picked up, intensifying the heat that pulsed between her legs. She squirmed and turned on her side, once more cuddling the pillow to her. So strong was his power of suggestion that all she could think of was his strong, raspy fingertips stroking her flesh, building the flame in her to a white-hot pitch. She bit her lip. She remembered his voice, his smell, his mouth on her breasts.

She heard a key in the lock, and the click of the door was loud in the silent room. Cathleen stiffened, startled from her sensual dreams. Eyes open, she watched the door open. A slit of light from the hall shone through as a man's form slipped inside. Her throat froze. She couldn't scream. Couldn't move. She could only watch as he slipped like a shadow across the room to her bed and loomed over her.

His hand reached down to grasp the top of her sheet, and, though she couldn't see his features, in that moment she recognized his form and movement. "Casey," she breathed.

His teeth gleamed in the dark as he flipped down the sheet, exposing her naked flesh. "You did what I asked."

"Of course." She lay unmoving under his gaze.

He reached behind the bed to pull the cord of the curtains, drawing them open so that the moonlight spilled palely across the bed, gleaming on her white body. Casey gazed at her as he tore off his clothes to reveal a body as aroused as hers. He sat beside her on the bed and stroked her breasts. "God, you're beautiful, Cathleen. You're lovelier than I remembered."

She raised her hands in mute invitation, opening herself to him. His fingers slid downward and dipped into the liquid desire of her femininity. "You're ready for me."

Cathleen dug her fingers into his shoulders, glorying in the muscle and sinew. "Please, Casey, take me."

He shivered violently at the soft plea of her voice and centered himself between her legs, his urgent flesh seeking its soft home. Cathleen gasped with pure satisfaction as he filled her. She squeezed tightly, as if she would never let him go, and he groaned. He rested on his arms above her, his chest and arms rigid with strain. His breath was harsh in his throat. She knew he was holding back a raging passion, wanting to bring her to her peak first. His concern pleased her, but she wanted no restraint, no reason tonight. She wanted to feel the depths of his wild, un-leashed desire.

"Don't hold back," she murmured, caressing the smooth skin of his arms and back. Much to her surprise, Cathleen urged him on in language which would have made her blush at any other time. Her blunt, unvarnished words seemed to excite him more than the touch of her hands on his skin. He surged into her, lost in the supreme wonder of his cresting passion, and his violent thrusts set off a rippling explosion within her. Casey sagged against her, and Cathleen gladly accepted his full weight, wrapping her arms around him tightly and murmuring his name over and over.

Casey nuzzled her neck. His skin was damp against hers, the hairs around the edge of his face and neck wet. Cathleen wove her fingers into his hair, aware of little but a deep contentment. He shifted his weight from her, taking it on his hip and elbow, but touching her at every possible point. "I think I could die a happy man right now," he murmured.

"I'd rather you didn't," Cathleen retorted, and he chuckled.

"Oh, baby, where'd you learn to talk like that?"

"You didn't seem to mind."

She felt his smile against her neck. "No, I didn't mind. Hearing your sweet voice say it, knowing I could excite you so you'd forget your usual modesty . . . Lord, no, I didn't mind."

He rolled onto his back, and Cathleen settled familiarly against his chest. Suddenly she sat up, full of mock indignation, hands on her hips. "Where did you come from? What kind of trick was that to play on me?"

Casey laughed. "You'd rather I'd really been in Nashville?"

"Of course not. But you nearly scared the life out of me when I heard you come in that door. You're lucky I didn't scream my head off. I thought I was about to get robbed or raped or killed."

Casey stroked her arm. "No. Only loved into a stupor."

"You aren't getting off that easily. How'd you get in here?"

"Dusty told the desk to give me a key to your room."

"They're pretty casual with keys to my room."

"Hell, they ate it up with a spoon. Wild sex among the country and western stars—they'll have quite a story to tell the next shift about how Dusty Richards arranged an affair for his daughter and C.J. Casey."

Cathleen giggled. "They're probably rock'n'roll fans and don't even know who we are. But what are you doing in New Orleans?"

"Isn't that obvious? I missed you, and I figured this was the perfect place to meet you, since you have a day off tomorrow before you continue the tour."

"You came all this way to spend one day with me?"

"And two nights," he reminded her, wiggling his eyebrows suggestively. "Sure I did. I *missed* you. And I didn't have anything else to do."

"Uh-huh. What about the new album you start cutting next week, the one you need to write two songs for?"

"I'll buy them from you. Honey, there's no way an album can compete with you."

Cathleen smiled, basking in his love.

They spent a wonderful day together in New Orleans, sightseeing, touring the clubs and returning to their hotel room to share another wondrous night together. All too quickly it was over. Casey flew back to Nashville, and Cathleen boarded the bus for the ride to Houston. In the days afterward there were times when she wished Casey hadn't visited her in New Orleans, because she seemed to miss him even more than she had before.

She was exhausted by the pace, and each night it became harder to create the inner charge necessary to attract and hold an audience. There were moments when the music pierced her soul, or she and Dusty sang together so well that she seemed to soar. But the pleasures were small compared to the fatigue and the aching emptiness in her chest. She wasn't made for the road, Cathleen decided. She needed peace and quiet, rest—a home and family.

No, she wouldn't let herself even dream about a home and family, at least not with Casey. Cathleen had violated many of her long-held beliefs for Casey, but she had to keep that one. Marriage couldn't stand up to the pressures of Casey's career, and she loved him too much to watch their love die on the rocky path of marriage, as her parents' had. Of course, she realized that the issue wasn't likely to come up, since she doubted that Casey would ask her to marry him. Somehow that reassurance didn't raise her spirits.

Their last concert was in Little Rock, Arkansas, and afterwards they would pile on the bus and drive straight home, too eager to reach Nashville to spend the night in Little Rock. Cathleen dressed and made up for the concert in better spirits than she had the past few nights. They were going home! No fans, no pressure, no sore throats from singing too long too often . . . and no more missing Casey. She smiled as she slipped into the black satin jumpsuit, which had become her favorite costume. She wore her hair naturally with it, because it called for simplicity. It had no frills or ornaments, just a superb fit that flattered her waist without broadening her hips and a luxurious material that glimmered as she moved.

Dusty had a costume to go with her black suit, and he wore it that night. The whole outfit was black—slacks, boots, felt hat and satin shirt. Over the shirt he wore a sleeveless quilted vest, also black. The lines delineating the padded cloth squares of the vest were sewn with flashing silver thread to catch the stage lights. The collar and cuffs of his shirt were also sewn with a delicate tracery of silver embroidery. He looked dark and dangerous in the suit, Cathleen thought, stepping into his dressing room before the show began. Dusty smiled at her in the mirror as he dabbed on the last of his makeup. The usual media people and privileged visitors were hanging around him, and he kept up a humorous bantering. But Cathleen detected the lines of strain in his face. The tour had taken its toll on him. He was older now, and maintaining his charismatic image was difficult without liquor. However, Cathleen reminded herself, he had won a great victory by sticking out the tour without once slipping back to his old drinking ways. She was proud of him, and finally convinced that he would be able to live out his life sober.

She went to him and squeezed his hand lovingly. He sensed her thoughts. "Been a hard road, huh?" he murmured.

"Yeah, but you made it."

Dusty closed his eyes, and for an instant his face was open and vulnerable. Then he opened his eyes and winked at her, the mask of charm restored. "Let me introduce you around."

Cathleen was no longer ill at ease with their visitors before the shows, and she chatted with them to take some of the pressure off Dusty. Soon the show began. Suddenly, as she waited in the wings for her entrance, it started to zip past all too fast. She had wanted it to end, was happy to go home, yet there was something sad about the final concert. Dusty called her name, and she strode onto the stage, smiling, to give herself up to the music. It turned out to be one of their best performances.

Afterwards they walked off the stage and down the hall past admiring fans. Smiling and signing autographs, they moved through the people, a little numbed by exhaustion and the knowledge that it was over. Finally Cathleen reached the quiet of her dressing room. She stripped off her heavy makeup and slid out of the jumpsuit. She dressed in comfortable cut-off shorts and a peasant blouse with a wide ruffle around the scoop neck. She slid her feet into sandals and carried her makeup bag out to the bus, again passing the gauntlet of well-wishers. When she reached the bus she handed the case to the driver with a sigh of relief and climbed the steps. She settled down with a pillow on one of the back seats, intending to sleep all the way home.

However, once the bus was loaded and started off with a

roar through the hushed night, she discovered that she was too excited to sleep. The others seemed to feel the same way. The continual poker game was going on. Dusty and Jim were smoking and talking in one corner. Only Joyce, who suffered from none of the adrenaline of a live performance, was sound asleep, leaving Cathleen without anyone to talk to. She had no desire to try to start a conversation with Vern, or the vapid girl he had picked up in Dallas and was apparently taking home with him. Cathleen considered joining Dusty, but decided that she'd rather sit alone with her thoughts. They were mostly of Casey. She wondered how he would react if she drove out to his farm as soon as she arrived in Nashville. Using the automatic gate opener and the house key he had given her, she could slip into his bedroom in the early morning hours and awaken him with kisses. For an instant the horrible thought flashed through her mind that perhaps he would have another woman in his bed, but she dismissed it. Casey wasn't dishonest. He had said he loved her, and she believed him. He wouldn't pick up another woman to fill his bed while she was gone for a month.

The more she thought about going to Casey the moment she got home, the more it appealed to her. She wouldn't be sleepy, because she would be too excited at the prospect of seeing him. It would be delightful to kiss him awake and see the pleasure dawn in his eyes. There was nothing as wonderful as an early morning homecoming.

Her thoughts slid back to her childhood and the times when Dusty would slip into her room, whispering, "Sweetpea, are you awake?"

Or the lights would come on all over the house, and Stella would traipse down the hall of the bedroom wing, a cardboard container holding exotic ice cream cones in her hands. "Are there any little girls in this house?" she would call, and Lynette and Cathleen would bounce out of their beds, breathless with joy and excitement. Cathleen remembered how beautiful Stella had always looked to her then. She knew now that her mother must have been tired from her tour, but her eyes had sparkled and her jewelry had seemed especially glittering in the night-dim rooms. She had been a lovely, foreign creature, and at times Cathleen had wondered how she had happened to land in their midst.

Stella would hug Lynette first, a fact Cathleen had accepted as natural, though there were times when she envied Lynette her superior status. Then Stella would turn to her and hold out her arms, and Cathleen would run to be engulfed in the sweet-smelling, richly appareled arms. That was how she had thought of her mother: sweet perfume, soft garments and a melodic, throaty voice.

She understood now, she thought, her parents' feelings when they returned from the tour. They must have been tired and ready to drop, yet eager to see their children again, as she was eager to be with Casey. Each time Dusty would vow he wouldn't go on tour again, but would stay home with his family. A month or two later, though, they would be gone again. Cathleen wondered how it felt to be torn by love for performing on one hand and love for one's family on the other. She had never thought of it from that point of view before, only from the perspective of the one who was left behind.

Her eyes closed, and she floated in a state between sleep and consciousness. She thought again of her mother and wondered if she had spoken the truth that night after Dusty's banquet. For a brief, semisweet moment she wished she were a little girl again and could run to her mother's arms. She would like to breathe in the scent and cool feel of her. . . . Cathleen drifted to sleep.

She didn't awaken until they reached Nashville, when the stirring around her and the lights flashing through the windows awakened her. She sat up and stretched, yawning and disoriented. It took her a moment to realize where she was. Then she scooted over to the window and pressed her nose to the glass. Yes, it really was Nashville. She grinned, and dug in her purse for a comb, mirror and lipstick, wide awake now and alive with expectation. When they reached Dusty's house Cathleen slipped off the bus and pulled out her car keys. She kissed Dusty on the cheek and told him that she was leaving the unloading of their baggage and instruments in his hands. Her father glanced at her, startled, but shrugged.

Cathleen hurried to her car and unlocked it. It started a little crankily after its long disuse, but was soon purring. She backed out, swerving to avoid the protruding rear of the bus. With a cheerful wave to her father and Rick, she zoomed away.

The ride to Casey's farm was exhilarating. Dawn tinged the eastern horizon with bright pink and gold. As she drove, the light crept up behind the layered clouds, turning them to pastel shades. The morning air was crisp and almost cool, not hot and muggy as it would be in a few hours, and Cathleen rolled down her window to enjoy it. When she reached the gates of the farm she pressed the remote control and swept through. She was driving too fast for the winding, narrow road, but she was too eager to be careful.

She parked beside the house and entered through the side door, which lay closest to Casey's room. She closed the door silently behind her and tiptoed across the tiled hall floor to his bedroom. The heavy drapes were drawn, casting the room into blackness. The plush carpet softened her footsteps as she advanced to the bed. For a moment she stood looking down at Casey, stealing a moment to admire him.

He was sprawled across the bed on his stomach, arms outspread and sheets tangled around his legs. His torso was naked, hinting of the same bareness lower on his body. His face was burrowed into the mattress, the thick black hair tangling around it. He twitched as she watched, then relaxed again. "Casey?" He stirred. Again she called his name, and he mumbled, rolling onto his back. His eyes opened to slits. When he saw her, his gaze sharpened and his eyes flew open wide.

"Cathy!" He reached out to pull her onto the bed with him. He didn't question the time or the suddenness of her appearance. Instead, he wrapped his arms around her and pressed her to his chest, burying his face in her hair. "Mmm, I'm glad you're home."

Cathleen lifted her head, and Casey kissed her on the mouth. She melted into him, giving herself up to the joy of his love.

Chapter 14

THEIR LOVEMAKING WAS SWIFT AND URGENT, IMPELLED BY strong mutual need, and afterwards they lay together, sated, drowsy, murmuring of their love and the pain of separation, until contentment lulled them to sleep. It was afternoon before Cathleen awoke. Tired and relaxed for the first time in weeks, she hadn't wakened when Casey rose and dressed. The heavy curtains kept out the sun, allowing her to sleep through the day. Finally noise from the kitchen awoke her. She sat up groggily and glanced around for Casey. The mussed bed was empty except for herself. Nor could she find him in the luxurious bathroom.

Shrugging, she popped into the shower for a quick wash, then put on some of the clothes she had taken to leaving in Casey's closet. Dressed in blue-and-white-striped seersucker shorts and a pale blue sleeveless blouse, she ventured out of the bedroom. Casey was easily discovered. She heard a loud clatter from the kitchen, followed by a vivid expletive. Cathleen giggled and followed the noise.

Casey swung around at her approach, and his face lit up.

"I was beginning to think you'd sleep all day." He pulled her into a bone-crushing hug. "I knew you were tired, but I selfishly hoped you'd wake up soon. I wanted to see you."

"Is that why you were clanging the pots and pans out here?" Cathleen teased.

Casey grimaced. "I gave Mrs. Andrews the day off because I wanted us to be alone. I was going to fix lunch. As I took the pot of soup off the stove, the potholder slipped. I burned my finger and dropped the pan." He looked ruefully at the pan lying on its side on the floor, soup puddling around it.

Cathleen giggled. "You made a nice mess." She took his hand and examined the burned finger, then brought it to her lips. "Does that make it better?"

He grinned. "It'll help."

They cleaned up the spill, and Cathleen made a quiche, declaring that she'd had enough canned and packaged foods on the tour. It was fun to cook again, and even more so to have Casey trailing her around the kitchen, caressing and kissing her at every turn. While the quiche baked they wandered into the large living area and sat down on the couch. Casey picked up her hand and caressed her fingers one by one, as if he had just discovered them.

"I was lonelier without you than I ever imagined I could be," he told her softly, warming her heart. She leaned her head on his shoulder. "Sweetheart, I have something to ask you."

"What?" she murmured.

"I want to marry you."

Cathleen stiffened as if she had touched a live wire, and her head snapped up. "What!"

He frowned at her, puzzled. "I said I want to marry you."

"You're crazy." She rose, pulling her hand from his grasp, and moved away from him.

"I know that. What does it have to do with marrying me?"

"We can't get married."

"Why not? Are we secretly related or something?"

"Don't be silly. Surely—you know how I feel!"

"You told me you didn't want to get involved with me. But you've already done that. I thought you'd gotten over your hangup."

"I haven't. And it's not a hangup. It's a rational decision, a . . . a choice of lifestyle."

"Lifestyle?" he repeated incredulously. "I'm talking about love and marriage, not some pseudopsychological theory. Cathy, you aren't seriously turning me down, are you?"

"Yes!" she flared, irritated by his assumption that she would accept his offer with glee. "If you'd even thought about what I've told you in the past, you'd have known I wouldn't want to marry you."

"I told you, I thought you'd gotten over that idiocy."

"Idiocy!"

"I didn't dream you'd object. You said you loved me, and I love you. I thought—I expected—damnation, Cathy, most women would be pleased by a proposal."

"Sorry I'm not properly impressed by your gracious offer to make an honest woman of me. I realize that there are dozens of women panting to take my place."

His jaw dropped, and Casey jumped up to face her, anger replacing astonishment. "What's gotten into you? This morning you were moaning with pleasure at my touch. Now you act as if you hate me."

"I don't hate you. But passion doesn't make a marriage."

"I'm not talking about passion alone. I was under the impression that we loved each other. I nearly went out of my skull, I missed you so much. You told me you missed me, too. Cathy, I love you. I want to share my life with you. I've never felt this way about anyone else."

Cathleen's face softened. "I'm sorry. I shouldn't have snapped. You startled me, and you sounded so smug and sure of yourself."

"I *was* sure. I thought our love was so strong that marriage was the obvious next step."

"It's not, not if we have any sense."

"What does sense have to do with it?"

"Unfortunately, not much, as far as most people are concerned. But I'm different. I'm not getting married because I'm swept away by emotion. We aren't good candidates for marriage. My parents are divorced, and my sister is *getting* divorced. *You're* divorced."

"That's in the past. It doesn't mean you and I can't make it work. Divorce isn't an inherited trait."

"I'm sure you thought you and your first wife wouldn't get divorced, either."

"That has nothing to do with it. If I'd loved her the way I love you, I'd have done anything to make our marriage work. As it was, I didn't care enough to try. Besides, I was younger then. I know more now. I can avoid the pitfalls."

"Love isn't enough. Dusty and Stella were crazy about each other, but that didn't stop them from tearing each other apart."

"I'm not Dusty, and you aren't Stella. We wouldn't have to follow their scenario. Love and a good marriage aren't mutually exclusive."

"No, but love doesn't ensure it, either. It's not enough to combat the pressures of the entertainment business. You're too much like Dusty."

"How?"

"You were one of his big drinking buddies, remember? You're charming, handsome, irresistible to women. You're an artist and have the temperament and problems of one."

"Sometimes I am moody and temperamental, but, honey, I'm mild compared to Dusty. You've gotten along with him all your life. You're used to dealing with singers. I'm not difficult to live with. You've been around me enough to know that. You also ought to have noticed that I'm not an alcoholic. I don't go out drinking with Dusty anymore. I grew up, even though he didn't. I get offers from women, but I don't have to accept. I have no need for casual sex. I've had that kind of life. It's not what I want. I haven't slept with another woman since I met you at Sunburst. Other women don't satisfy me. Only you."

"Right now that's true."

"Are you going to hide your head in the sand and ignore every opportunity for a happy life because things might change in the future?" he thundered. "Nothing's perfect, Cathy. Marriages don't come with a guarantee. Can't you take things as they are?"

Cathleen stared at him mutinously, her jaw set. He didn't understand. He'd never witnessed the hell of a marriage founded on love and destroyed by jealousy, temper and the demands of a career. Casey sighed and shoved his hands into his already tousled hair. He stood for a moment, thinking, then dropped his hands to his sides.

"Things have to be perfect for you, don't they? Life, people, everything. If they aren't, you reject them. You cut Stella out of your life because she wasn't the best mother. You're scared of the music business because it has problems. And you're scared of marriage for the same reason. Why can't you take things as they are? Why can't you accept life and people as imperfect and go on, risks and all?"

"Why can't *you* accept things as they are?" Cathleen retorted. "You're the one who wants to change things. We could go on as we have been, seeing each other whenever we want, loving each other, being happy."

"Relationships stagnate if they don't go forward. We can't sit in the same place forever. We have to move to another level. Commit ourselves. Love doesn't stay in the same place. It grows or it dies."

Cathleen began to tremble. "Then . . . then you're saying that if I won't marry you, that's the end of us?"

He hesitated, his hands balled into fists. "Yes, that's what I'm saying. Either you love me enough to marry me, or our love is a sham."

She was stunned, numb. Slowly Cathleen turned and walked away, trailing out of the living area and down the hall to Casey's bedroom. She picked her purse up from the floor where she had dropped it the previous night and went to the side door. There was no sound from the rest of the house. Casey wasn't following her, wasn't calling to her to stop. He meant what he had said. He was kicking her out of his life because she wouldn't marry him. She turned the doorknob and walked out.

Her shoes crunched on the gravel. She stepped into her car and started the engine, backing onto the circular drive. The house was still. No sign of Casey. She drove down the narrow road and out the wide gates at the end. She punched the button of the remote control and watched the gates slowly shut behind her. Suddenly her eyes filled with tears. She leaned her head on the steering wheel and dissolved into sobs. It was over. Over.

Cathleen finally started the car again and drove home. Her head ached dully, and her eyes were red and swollen. She hoped no one would be home when she got there, so she could go straight to her bedroom without having to explain her puffy face and red eyes. She groaned when she turned onto her street and saw Jack Beaudry's car in front of her house. Dusty's car and Lynette's were sitting on the driveway. Everyone was there. She wondered if there was any way she could slip through the kitchen and down the hall to her bedroom without being spotted.

She couldn't, of course. As she closed the door Lynette called to her. Cathleen sighed and went into the den to greet them, bracing for the inevitable questions. As it turned out, there were none. Dusty sat on the sofa, looking slightly stunned. Jack and Lynette sat opposite him, Jack in a big easy chair and Lynette perched on the wide, flat arm of it. They were too full of their own news to notice Cathleen's state.

"Guess what!" Lynette jumped up, grinning.

"I don't know. What?"

"Jack and I are engaged."

For a long moment Cathleen stared uncomprehendingly. Lynette's statement was so far from anything she had expected that her mind couldn't make sense of the words. When they finally sank in, she felt as if her knees might give way. She'd had too many shocks today. "What? You're—Lynette, are you joking?"

"No!" Lynette denied indignantly. She turned to Jack. "You tell her. Maybe she'll believe you."

Jack nodded. "She's right, Cathy. We're engaged."

"But when . . . how . . . I didn't know there was anything between you."

Lynette giggled. "Oh, Cathy, it was so obvious. You would have guessed for sure if you hadn't been wrapped up in your own love life. Jack and I have been together practically all the last month."

Cathleen wet her lips and tried to pull her thoughts together. It was wild. Jack was years older than Lynette. She herself thought of him as her father's contemporary. After all, he'd known them since she and Lynette were children. Lynette wasn't divorced yet. "It's been such a short time."

"It can happen that way," Lynette responded gaily. She took her sister's hand. "Come on. I have to get dressed. We're going out. Why don't you talk to me while I'm getting ready?"

Cathleen followed Lynette, her own pain receding as curiosity about her sister took over. After they entered Cathleen's bedroom, Lynette began to brush her long chestnut hair and arrange it in a knot atop her head. "Isn't it crazy? Jack Beaudry is the last person I'd have dreamed I would fall in love with."

"I'm having difficulty absorbing it," Cathleen admitted. She hesitated. "Lynette, he wasn't one of the men you were seeing . . . I mean, before you left Michael."

"Heavens, no! Can you imagine Jack involved in anything illicit? Besides, I told you, none of them made me happy. Falling in love with Jack happened since I came here. He took me places, trying to get my mind off Michael and my divorce. I didn't think anything of it. He was only a friend of Dusty's. In fact, I think he took me out more to keep me out of your hair than anything else.

Then one day I looked at him, and I started thinking how cute he was, how sexy."

"Jack?" Cathleen's voice registered her astonishment.

Lynette giggled. "He's not a hunk like Casey. But there's something appealing about him. He gets a lazy look in his eye that sends shivers down my spine. I was appalled when I started wondering what he'd be like in bed. He was Dusty's friend! I guess it hit him, too, 'cause one day we were over at his apartment talking, and he said something funny. I couldn't stop laughing. I grabbed his arms to help me stand up. He kissed me. And, oh, Cathy, it was so marvelous! Well, it went from there."

"But marriage?" Cathleen protested. "You don't have your divorce yet."

"We'll wait for a few months after the divorce. Jack insists—to make sure I feel the same. He's afraid what I feel for him is backlash from my divorce. I know it's not. With Jack, I have what I never did with Michael or any of those others. I told Jack about the other men, but he loves me anyway. He *knows* me, right down to my toes, and he still loves me."

"There's a big difference in your ages."

"Not so much. I'm twenty-eight. He's forty-two. It's only fourteen years."

"Only?"

"It's not like we're different generations, or he's old enough to be my father. He said I wanted a father figure. I told him I had all the father I could handle in Dusty. I don't need another one. I know Jack's older, but we fit together. He understands me and my background. I know his world. I'm where I belong."

"But a singer? He's the opposite of what you always wanted."

"Being married to Michael changed my mind. I know the dangers of marriage to a country and western singer. I can handle them. I won't be lost like I was in Michael's world. When I married Michael, I was running away from myself. But Jack—Jack's what I am. Even if we fell apart like Dusty and Stella, at least I would have had something. With Michael, I had nothing."

Lynette finished her hairdo and makeup and began to sort through the clothes in her closet. Cathleen closed her eyes. It was incredible, but Lynette was so happy that it couldn't be wrong. She rose and hugged her sister. "I'm glad. I hope you'll be very happy."

Lynette smiled joyfully. "I will be."

"I'll let you get dressed. I have to congratulate Jack." Cathleen returned to the den. Dusty was slumped on the couch, his feet stretched out, and he was contemplating the pointed toes of his cowboy boots. Jack stood by the back window. When she entered, they turned to her and smiled.

"I tell you, Cathleen," Dusty said in a teasing voice. "My old buddies are taking my girls away from me. First Casey grabs you. Now Jack decides to marry Lynette. I told him, it's downright impolite."

His remark about Casey reopened the wound of their parting, but Cathleen forced a smile. Now was not the time to throw gloom over everything. "You'll have to go find some young girl, too," she joked.

Jack grinned and winked. "Hell, Dusty knows no young girl will have him."

Cathleen went to Jack and took his hand in hers. "I want to wish you the best."

His eyebrows rose comically. "You don't think I'm an old fool?"

Cathleen shook her head. "Never. Lynette is ecstatic. I can't argue with that."

"There are a lot of things against it. Sometimes I think I'm crazy. We're waiting a year, so Lynette can be sure this isn't a rebound from her divorce."

"I don't think it is."

"That night when Lynette and her husband were arguing, I wanted to knock him to kingdom come. I didn't realize why I disliked him. I'd known you and Lynette since you were kids. I felt like your uncle or something.

Then you walked in with Casey. Anybody could tell you'd been making love. For a minute, I was sick. I still thought of you as a little girl. It was as if Casey had molested a child. That night I figured out why it upset me. Then I accepted that you and Lynette weren't children anymore. After that, I couldn't look at her in the same way. I realized how beautiful and desirable she was. I wanted her. I fell in love, but I figured she wouldn't look at me. When I found out she felt the same way, it blew me away." He smiled and shook his head. "We probably seem foolish to you, don't we? You always have your feet on the ground."

Tears clogged Cathleen's throat. "No, not always."

"Well, sometimes I think we are crazy. But I figure you have to take risks or you might as well give up and die. You *are* dead. They just haven't put you in the ground. I don't want to spend the rest of my life regretting what I didn't do."

Was everyone else crazy, Cathleen wondered, for choosing love despite the dangers? Or was she the one who was crazy, for holding back?

Days passed and turned into weeks. Cathleen didn't see or hear from Casey. Every time the telephone rang she jumped for it, her heart racing. Maybe it would be Casey asking her to return, agreeing to live as they had before. But it never was. Several times a day she almost called him to admit that she couldn't live without him. But each time she stopped, reminding herself that the pain she felt now would be nothing compared to the agony of a marriage falling apart. It was better to let it die now.

Lynette was often gone with Jack, and after a few days of rest after the tour, Dusty, too, usually left the house. Casey's absence was too noticeable for them to ignore, and each tentatively asked Cathleen about it. She responded by saying that she didn't want to discuss it, and they turned away, relieved. Cathleen was left alone with her thoughts. They were racking companions. Casey's words haunted her as much as she missed him. She wondered if she were as frightened and demanding as he'd painted her. Did she expect people and things to be perfect? Did she abandon them when they weren't? Was she wise not to marry Casey, or merely a coward?

She tried to write songs, but her pain was too fresh and strong to be put down on paper. Maybe later, but not yet. She wondered about her career. "Dreamer" had topped the charts while she and Dusty were on tour. Soon Sunburst would release another of Dusty's singles and one of her solos. John Metcalf urged her to cut another record with them. She enjoyed singing, but a career in it had always been anathema to her. She had hated the grind of touring. Could she take the life? Or should she stick to writing songs?

As the days passed, Casey's proposal and singing became tangled in her mind, along with her rejection of Stella. They seemed part of the same problem. Either she was justified in refusing them, or she was frightened and isolated, unwilling to take risks and enjoy life. Angrily she pushed away the doubts Casey had raised. Casey just wanted his way, no matter what she desired or needed. He would take nothing less than her commitment to him, heart and soul. She couldn't give him that. She just couldn't!

Wrapped up in her own troubles, she saw no warning signs of what was coming. Later, she wasn't sure whether there had been any warning. Perhaps a volcano had been building in Dusty that she should have seen. Or it could have been a spur of the minute thing, a snap decision that even Dusty hadn't suspected.

Cathleen had driven to Murfreesboro and back that afternoon, hoping that the change of scenery would cheer her, but the drive had lifted her spirits only a little. She sighed, thinking of another lonely evening. If only she could stop missing Casey! If only she didn't desire him, didn't remember the way he looked or the things he said to her. . . . If only her blood didn't heat up at the thought of him, making it impossible to sleep at night.

Dusty's car wasn't in the driveway when she drove in,

and nobody answered her call as she walked in the back
door. She drooped. She had hoped that Lynette or Dusty
would be there to help keep her mind off Casey. She
opened the refrigerator and took out a soft drink. She had
her finger inside the ring to open the can before the view in
front of her registered on her brain. It was something so
familiar to her in the past she didn't notice it at first, but
also so foreign now that shock waves ran through her.
There were two cans of beer on the top shelf, the empty
plastic rings mute evidence of four missing cans.

Cathleen began to tremble. She sat down abruptly. No!
Dusty couldn't have started drinking again. Maybe it was
Vern, or somebody who had come to visit Dusty and
brought his beer along. She scurried to the trash can and
lifted the swinging lid. An aluminum can flashed in the
light. She made a slow examination of the room and
spotted another can on the far counter by the sink. But
that didn't prove that Dusty had drunk it. It didn't mean
Dusty had fallen off the wagon. Even if he had drunk one
beer with someone, it didn't make him a drunkard again.

A sob rose in her throat. She couldn't lie to herself.
Once Dusty started, he couldn't stop. She ran to his
bedroom, calling his name, her heart knocking against her
ribs. He wasn't there. The door stood wide open, and she
stepped inside cautiously. Another empty beer can stood
on Dusty's dresser. She picked it up and her hand closed
unconsciously around it, crumpling the thin aluminum.

It couldn't be. She wouldn't let it be. If she could find
Dusty, catch him before he was too far gone, the situation
would be salvageable. She spun and raced to the kitchen.
She found the dog-eared address book where she kept the
phone numbers of friends and acquaintances. In all likelihood, her father was at a friend's house, particularly if he
hadn't started drinking heavily. Her first hope was that he
was with Jack, who would do his best to end the drinking
and sober him up. She dialed his number. There was no
answer.

She hung up. She hadn't really expected to find him

there. Dusty would be as aware as she was that Jack would discourage his drinking. Besides, Lynette was with Jack. No, Dusty wouldn't go there. Vern. He was the likeliest person. She flipped through the pages and found his name scrawled in Dusty's writing on the inside of the back cover. With shaking fingers she dialed the number. Again there was no answer.

That wasn't good. Deep down she suspected that he was with Vern. If they weren't at either man's home, they were hanging around a bar. He'd be harder to find, and drunker. It was part of Dusty's pattern. However, she wasn't going to lose hope until she had contacted everyone else she could think of. Patiently she spent the next twenty minutes making phone calls. A few didn't answer. The rest hadn't seen Dusty. Finally she admitted defeat and tossed the battered book onto the counter. Tears burned at the backs of her eyes. "Daddy, how could you do this?" she whispered.

Cathleen dug her hands into her hair, pressing her fingers against her scalp as if to hold down the anger and betrayal boiling inside her. She wanted to scream. Not again. She simply could not take it if he started drinking. Her emotions were too raw because of Casey. Casey. She whirled back to the telephone and dialed his number. When his familiar voice answered she sagged with relief. For an instant she couldn't speak for the tears clogging her throat, and he repeated impatiently, "Hello?"

"Casey?"

"Cathleen! Is that you?"

"Yes. I . . . I—oh, Casey, I think Dusty's gone off the wagon."

"Oh, no." There was no surprise in his tone, only weariness and resignation. Cynically Cathleen thought that it was the reaction of someone who knew alcoholics— you prayed for miracles and expected the worst. "What happened?"

"I don't know. I came home and found a couple of beer cans in the refrigerator. There was an empty can in his bedroom, and Dusty was gone. I've called everyone I could think of, but I couldn't catch him. Vern's not at home, either."

Casey's description of Vern was explicit and unprintable. Cathleen agreed wholeheartedly. "Do you have any idea where he might be?" Casey asked.

"A bar, I guess."

"Hang on. I'll be right there."

Cathleen made no protest. Everything inside her cried out for his support and comfort. She made her way into the den and sat down to wait for Casey. She ached to cry, but she had long ago cried out her tears over Dusty. All that was left was a void.

She was unaware of how long she sat until she heard the screech of tires in the driveway. That must be Casey. She glanced at her watch. He'd made it from his house to hers in record time. She rose and started toward the kitchen just as Casey burst through the door. Without thinking Cathleen ran to him, and he enfolded her in his arms, cradling her tenderly against his chest, stroking her hair and murmuring words of comfort. Cathleen relaxed, soaking in his strength.

For a moment Dusty's problem receded. Casey was uppermost in her mind, as he had been for weeks. It felt so right to be in his arms, so good. Why couldn't things be different? Why did he have to want marriage and commitment? If only they could go along as they had been . . . she wrenched her thoughts away and stepped out of his arms. This was no time to be worrying about that again. She had to think of Dusty. Cathleen cleared her throat and crossed her arms over her chest. "Thank you for coming, Casey." Her words sounded ridiculously stilted and formal, even to herself. "I . . . uh . . . think I better search the bars. Maybe if I catch him soon enough . . . Will you come with me?"

He frowned. "Of course."

"I can use the help if he's very drunk."

"You can also use the emotional support. Why do you

hate to admit it? Are you afraid of getting too involved?" he gibed.

"If you're going to be nasty, I can get along without you!" Cathleen flared.

He raised his hands in an exculpatory gesture. "Okay, I'm sorry. Let's go."

Cathleen grabbed her purse, and they left the house. She directed Casey to their first stop. Although it wasn't Dusty's favorite hangout, it was on their way to the others. When they pulled up in front of it she discovered that it had closed down during the time Dusty was sober. They drove on. It was a long, boring search. They toured the parking lot of each bar, looking for Dusty's car. On their fourth stop Cathleen spotted the pale blue Cadillac. Casey pulled into a parking space, and they went inside.

There was no sign of Dusty. Casey asked the bartender whether he had seen Dusty. "Sure," the man replied laconically as he drew another beer. "He was in here with a couple of his friends."

"When?"

"They left about an hour ago."

"His car's still in the lot."

The man behind the bar shrugged. "Dusty was feeling no pain. Good thing if somebody else drove."

Cathleen's heart sank.

"You know where they were going?"

"Another place, I guess. One of 'em was complaining 'cause he wanted to shoot some pool. Don't know why. He was too pie-eyed to see the ball, let alone hit it."

Casey thanked the man for his time, folded a bill and laid it on the bar. He steered Cathleen outside. "You want to drive his car home?"

"No. Let's find him first and come back for the car. It'll be easier than driving two cars to all his spots."

"We could go home and wait for him to call, or one of the boys to drop him off. It sounds like he's too far gone for us to rescue him tonight."

It was tempting to give up on Dusty and head home.

She'd done it many times in the past. But she shook her head stubbornly. "No. We're scheduled on the Grand Ole Opry tomorrow night. I don't want him to miss a performance. At this point in his career, it could ruin him. Besides, I don't want him in Vern's company for a minute longer than it takes us to find them. If we can get him home and sober him up, maybe he won't fall off permanently. I'll take him to the Villa tomorrow to see his counselor."

"You're the boss. Where shall we go next?"

They tried three more honky-tonks before they found him. He and his friends were in the back, at the pool tables. Two of his good-time buddies were engaged in what they optimistically termed "playing pool." Their game consisted mostly of sprawling over the table, laughing uncontrollably. Dusty and Vern had given up trying to shoot and were seated on the floor beside the table, drinks in hand. When they looked up and saw Casey and Cathleen looming over them, Dusty's eyes shifted guiltily before he mustered his bravado. "Uh-oh," he said in a stage whisper to Vern. "It's the law."

"Hey, Cathy, how you doing?" Vern asked cheerfully and swept his half-empty glass in a wide arc. "Sit down and join us."

"No, thank you," Cathleen snapped, favoring the man with a look of purest rage. "You did this to him, didn't you? You're the meanest, lowest man I know. You can't stand for anyone else to be a success, can you?"

"Why you little—" he began, his eyes flashing ferally as he started to rise. Casey extended a foot and gave him a lazy push against the shoulder. He fell back heavily.

"Don't push me, Vern," Casey warned. "It's one of my policies not to get into barroom brawls, but you're someone I'd love to make an exception for."

"Come on, Case, why're you getting excited?" Vern retreated into a whine. "So the man had a few drinks. What's the harm? It won't hurt him to tie one on now and then."

"Maybe it wouldn't hurt some people," Cathleen retorted heatedly, "but you know Dusty's not one of them."

Dusty struggled to his feet, facing his daughter with a dignity that would have been ludicrous had it not been so pitiful. "I am your father, young lady. I'll thank you to treat me with more respect."

"When you deserve it, I will!" Cathleen's eyes spat fire, and she literally shook with the force of her anger, disillusionment and pain.

"Come on, darlin', that's enough." Casey curved an arm around her shoulders and drew her close. "No point getting into hair pulling right here. Let's take Dusty home." He grasped Dusty's elbow. "Come on, old buddy."

"I'm not going anywhere." Dusty dug in his heels mulishly.

"Go on to the car, Cath," Casey instructed. "Dusty and I'll be there in a minute."

Cathleen was relieved to turn the situation over to Casey. She left without a murmur, almost running from the bar. Casey turned to Dusty. His sinewy fingers dug into the other man's arms. "If it was up to me, I'd leave you to stew in your own juice. After the time, effort and emotions Cathleen's wasted on you, your doing this was like kicking her in the gut. Personally, I wouldn't waste my time on you. But for some reason that lady loves you and hopes she can make something of you. She wants you to come home. So that's what you're doing."

Vern wavered to his feet. "He's a grown man. Let him do what he wants. Come on, Dusty, you don't have to go with him. Billy? Murphy?" He spoke over his shoulder to the two at the pool table. "We got a man here who thinks he can make Dusty leave when he don't want to."

Casey rolled his eyes. "Give me a break. The condition you guys are in, Cathleen could deck you. Come on, Dusty."

"Okay, okay." Dusty tried to brush him off. "I can walk out on my own."

"I'm not so sure about that," Casey responded, but released him. Dusty began a weaving progress from the bar. Casey faced Vern, his expression hard. "Listen. You

aren't worth stomping. But if I ever—*ever*—hear that
you've been out drinking with Dusty Richards again, I
promise you you'll be dead in this business. If I drop a hint
in a few people's ears, you won't work in Nashville again.
If your brains haven't completely turned to mush, you
know I can do it. Do you hear me?"

"Yeah, I hear you," Vern responded sullenly.

"Good. Remember it next time you feel inclined to pull
Dusty down with you." Casey turned on his heel and
strode out of the room.

Chapter 15

CASEY SLID BEHIND THE DRIVER'S SEAT OF HIS CAR. Cathleen was leaning back in her seat, eyes closed. Her face was drawn. Dusty, his good humor recovered, rested against one door of the rear seat, his legs stretched out before him. He sang a Hank Williams song, forgetting half the words and substituting his own words or nonsense syllables to maintain the rhythm. Casey wrinkled his nose. "God, Dusty, you smell like the inside of a whiskey barrel. What have you been drinking?"

"Boilermakers." Dusty gave the popular name for shots of whiskey followed by beer chasers.

Casey groaned. "You don't do anything by halves, do you?"

Dusty shook his head with the comic gravity of a drunk. "Moderation's never been my strong suit," he admitted. Casey barely suppressed a chuckle. Even Cathleen had to smile.

"Oh, Daddy," she murmured, laughter mingling with tears in her voice, "what am I going to do with you?"

Dusty didn't hear her. He was off on another song, this one an ancient railroading tune by Jimmy Rodgers. Casey took Cathleen's hand, but she didn't return his pressure. She was wrapped up in the isolation that was her usual response to Dusty's drinking. Casey glanced over and realized that though she was physically in the car, she had withdrawn mentally, cutting herself off from pain and loss—and comfort. His forehead wrinkled. Casey said nothing more to her on their journey.

He stopped at the bar they had visited earlier, and Cathleen hopped out to drive Dusty's car home. Casey followed her. When she pulled into the drive, Casey behind her, Cathleen saw that the house was still dark. Lynette wasn't home yet. She checked her watch and saw that it was only ten o'clock. The stress of the evening made it seem far later.

She left the car and hurried up the steps to unlock the side door. She started back to help Casey, but he had Dusty well in hand. He clasped one strong arm around Dusty's torso, and clamped the other on Dusty's arm to hold it in place around his shoulders. Dusty, a gregarious drunk, had bullied Casey into singing along, and both their voices were raised in a mournful Jim Reeves ballad.

"No living artists tonight, I see," Cathleen commented crisply.

"No. It seems to be an evening of tributes. Maybe we'll do Patsy Cline next," Casey joked.

Dusty shook his head seriously. "Nope. Out of my range."

Cathleen held the door open for them. "At least Casey remembers the lyrics."

Casey guided the older man's wavering steps through the kitchen and down the hall to his bedroom, ignoring Dusty's attempts to wander into the den. Cathleen followed grimly. Casey turned at the door to Dusty's bedroom. "I'll put him down."

Cathleen hesitated, grateful to be relieved of the chore, but feeling that it was too great a burden to put on anyone who wasn't related to Dusty. "I've done it lots of times."

"I've done it a few times myself." He grunted as Dusty suddenly sagged against him. "Looks like the time is upon us. Sit down and rest. I'll handle it."

Cathleen didn't protest a second time. She went into the den and sank onto the couch, massaging her temples. She was beyond thought, aware only of tremendous despair and the old, familiar fear—a terror so deep and pervading that it had no name or identifiable focus. Unbidden, the thought of Stella came into her mind. Cathleen wanted to call her. She froze, her muscles tensed to rise and go to the telephone.

Then she shook her head, repelling the idea. Things were getting bad if she was thinking of running to Stella with her problems.

Rapid footsteps sounded in the hall, and Casey entered the room. "He shouldn't cause you any more trouble tonight."

"Thank you. I—I appreciate your help."

"I don't mind."

She wished she could break into tears and hold on to Casey for comfort, but she'd found out long ago that there was no comfort—and no use for tears. Casey made an irritated noise deep in his throat and hauled her to her feet, tilting her head back so she was forced to stare into his face. He was so near that her rebellious senses yearned for him, seeking his familiar, delightful scent and feel. Sternly she reminded herself that they were through. It had been foolish to call him. She should have hunted for Dusty alone, but she had yielded to her weakness and reached out for Casey. Damn! Why couldn't she manage on her own anymore? She had done it for years before Casey. How had he made her dependent on him in such a short time?

"Come on, Cath, talk to me," he ordered hoarsely. "You're like a zombie."

"I'm tired." She ran a weary hand through her hair.

"It's only ten."

"These scenes with Dusty wear me out."

"That's because you invest so much of yourself in

them." His fingers dug in sharply. "Why, Cathleen? Why
do you give everything to Dusty and leave nothing for
yourself or me?"

"Casey, please, let's not have an argument tonight. I
don't have the energy."

"You don't have the energy or the interest or the
desire . . ." he spat out and released her suddenly. He
spun and strode away, jamming his hands into the rear
pockets of his jeans. "I swear to God, Cathy, I think I'd
kill that man if it would release you from this self-imposed
bondage."

"I don't know what you're talking about."

"The hell you don't!" He whirled back to her, his eyes
bright with anguished rage. "I'm talking about the way
you give and give and give to Dusty, never taking anything
in return. You let him drain you until there's no room in
your life for your own needs and desires."

"You're crazy," Cathleen interrupted abruptly. "Just
because I don't want to marry you doesn't mean I have
some . . . some perverted tie to my father!"

"Maybe not perverted sexually, but it sure as hell has
twisted your emotions. You know what I think? I think
Dusty's sucked the life out of you, like he's tried to do with
everyone else close to him."

"That's not true! He hasn't—"

"Hasn't he? Then why are you scared to give? Why,
when you've got such beauty, such love and talent, do you
refuse to show it? You deny your innermost being, and
what other reason could there be except you're scared of
losing your soul? That's the thing Dusty's tried to pull out
of you, isn't it? Oh, Cathy, you have so much strength to
have given everything to Dusty all your life and yet not be
dead inside. Surely you have the strength to open yourself
to the good in love. I love you." He walked toward her
slowly, his gaze hypnotic, drawing her in. "I'm no Dusty. I
don't just take. I'll return everything you give me—and
double it. I want to love you, not use you or consume
you."

He stopped inches from her, so close that the heat radiating from his body touched her. Her breath came in short gasps. Cathleen couldn't think, couldn't speak, could only stare as his bright blue eyes loomed closer. His lips touched hers lightly, and she closed her eyes, trembling with the sweet onrush of feeling. Her body and heart cried out for him. She felt torn in two. His mouth brushed hers again, then settled in to prove his love. Her body was all fire and ice, thrilling, clashing, shivering on the brink of a feeling so huge it terrified her. Casey's tongue traced her lower lip and moved on to her short, vulnerable upper lip, then dipped into her opened mouth to taste the honey of her kiss.

Light as moth's wings, his hands grazed her arms and back, touching her everywhere. Her knees began to buckle, and his arms went around her to hold her up. His lips melded with hers, giving, demanding, seeking almost desperately. He broke away to nuzzle her cheek and throat, rediscovering the wonder of her silken skin. "I love you. I love you," he murmured feverishly. "Please, Cathy, come home with me. Let me make love to you. Let me . . ." One arm took her weight and the other hand slid up to find her breasts, caressing the soft, succulent mounds with swelling passion.

"Casey," she breathed, swaying and lost beneath the expert ministrations of his fingers.

He delved into her blouse, straining the buttonholes until they gave way and the buttons slipped through. He unfastened the front catch of her bra and impatiently shoved aside the loose halves so he could cup one breast. He lifted her as his head bent to the pleasures of her bared breasts. The twin peaks turned to hard cores of joy as his tongue bathed them with fire. Stroking, lashing, tickling, his tongue lingered over first one nipple, then the other, tapping the vein of desire repressed since Cathleen had walked out of his house weeks ago.

She was almost mindless with yearning, twisting beneath his hands and straining to find an outlet for her passion, too long denied. Suddenly the dam within her broke, and she pressed into Casey, writhing with a hunger which he'd merely scratched the surface of before. Cathleen wrapped her arms tightly around his neck, lifting herself to encircle his waist with her legs. He shuddered, his desire vaulted almost out of control by the intimacy of her body pressed against him. He raised his head to kiss her. Her lips seared into his, wild and seeking.

Casey sank slowly to his knees, carrying her with him to the floor without breaking the fiery seal of their mouths. Her hands roamed his body, impatiently popping the snaps of his western-style shirt to explore his naked chest. She was eager and wild, wanton—and he ached for her more than he ever had. Instinctively Casey knew that he had broken through her barriers, but he was too afire to think about it. There was nothing in him but the blissful torment of their fervid lovemaking.

They rolled across the floor, locked tightly in each other's arms, their mouths grinding and twisting together as if to consume each other. Her hips circled against his suggestively, and he let out an almost animal moan. His words were incoherent as he shoved aside the loose folds of her skirt to find her delicate lace underthings and drag them downward. But his mouth spoke volumes silently as he trailed it over the smooth skin of her chest, crossing the brief interruption of her skirt, and feasted on the nectared softness below. His tongue loved her as his maleness longed to, and the substitution tortured him even as it gave him pleasure.

He fumbled at the fastenings of his trousers as he parted her legs and moved in between them, but her hands stopped him. She rose lithely, so close to him that she was a second skin, and trailed her strong, supple fingers down his back. She cupped his hips, and pressed him even more intimately against her. He sucked in his breath in surprised pleasure. She kneaded the softness, so at odds with the rest of his lean, hard body, until he trembled and groaned. "Please, Cath, I can't—ah, so good. Let me—"

She shook her head and slipped her hands in between them. They played across his chest, tweaking a hair, arousing his masculine nipples, lightly scraping downward to the heavy waistband of his denim trousers. She slipped her fingers inside the waistband and he waited, eyes closed, hardly breathing as he waited for her next move. He was driven to a frenzy by her unexpected aggressiveness, but he strained to retain a grip on his control. He wanted to feel the full pleasure of her appetite.

She moved her hands back up to his chest and pushed lightly. Casey acquiesced, letting her press him onto his back on the floor. Then she returned to the snap of his jeans and unfastened both it and the zipper. She peeled down both underwear and jeans with one liquid movement. Again an animal moan was torn from him, but Casey made no move except to wet his parched lips and link his hands firmly behind his neck. Cathleen inched backward, stripping off his trousers as she went. She tossed the jeans and underwear on the floor and pulled off his socks and boots. Her breasts bobbed slightly with her exertions, and he lifted his head from the floor to watch. The sides of her unfastened blouse teased him, opening to reveal the pink crowns of her breasts with their hard, proud centers, then closing again to conceal them from his gaze. He felt the material graze against the tips as if it were his own fingers touching them.

Cathleen lifted one of his bare feet and kissed the sole, her tongue stealing out to tickle and tease. Casey shot up to a sitting position, his entire body jolted as if by electricity. Cathleen ignored him and kissed each of his toes as her thumbs kneaded the bottoms of his feet.

"Cathy, you're killing me."

She paused, and her smile was wickedly innocent. "Do you want me to stop?"

"Don't you dare," he growled.

She repeated her actions on his other foot before starting a slow climb up his legs, her body slithering sinuously over his. Her mouth traveled over him, sucking,

sliding, as she made circles with her tongue. He dug his
hands into her hair as his body arched convulsively. His
voice was harsh as gravel as he ground out her name. His
hands went to her hips, brooking no disobedience as he
moved her upward and settled her onto him. Cathleen
smiled down at him as she began her ride of love, her
pleasure enhanced by witnessing the sweet contortions of
desire on his face.

Suddenly Casey was pounding and churning, and his
strong arms gripped hers as his head rolled from side to
side; he was lost to everything but the explosion within
him. Cathleen clamped her legs around him, moving with
him, and the white-hot fire inside her tightened into a
small, hard knot, then burst outward. No ripples these,
but surging, roaring waves that washed through her body
to her extremities, then receded slowly, leaving behind the
complete relaxation of contentment. She went limp
against him, and Casey wrapped his arms around her,
holding her tightly against his damp chest.

For a long time Cathleen lay in a blissful fog, but
gradually the realization of where she was crept into her
mind. She sat up with a startled exclamation, shattering
their peaceful world. "Oh! Look where we are!"

Casey smiled languidly. "It doesn't matter."

"Doesn't matter?" she repeated in amazement. "We're
in the middle of the den floor, where Dusty or Lynette and
Jack could walk in on us at any moment."

"Believe me, Dusty's down for the count. Surely
Lynette and Jack would have some consideration for
lovers." He propped himself up on his elbows to watch
her, his eyes gleaming devilishly. "Girl, you're hell on
wheels. Did you know you melted my bones?"

"Casey . . ." Cathleen pulled on her underwear and
stood up to straighten her skirt. She clasped the plastic clip
fastening her bra and began to button her blouse. The top
two buttonholes had been stretched beyond repair and
gaped open despite her efforts to arrange the lapels. Casey
sighed and rolled to his feet. He slid into his discarded

clothes and raked his hands through his thick hair, stretching, then sat down to pull on his socks and boots.

Cathleen retreated to a chair, her mind jumbled and disoriented. What had just happened was incredible, insane. How could she have exploded into passion like that, crawling all over Casey and making love to him with wild abandon? Though she had always responded to Casey eagerly, she had never felt such driving need and hunger. She had wanted him to bury himself in her, for them to join together with such fire that they melted into each other. Casey's earlier assessment of her had been correct. Usually she guarded her emotions against the world, protecting her inner self from the demands and pulls of others. Yet tonight she had given herself utterly, and taken from him in the same manner.

Casey yawned so wide that it seemed his jaw would crack, and rubbed the back of his neck with one hand. "Let's go home, baby."

Cathleen froze. "Wait a minute. I—what happened just now—"

He grinned, waiting. "Yeah?"

"Don't look so smug!" she snapped, irritated by his complacent presumption that her objections to him had been overcome by their lovemaking. "That"—she motioned at the floor where they had lain—"didn't change anything."

"No?" He was still smiling, relaxed.

"No! I'm not going to marry you, Casey. I've told you. Just because you caught me in a weak moment—"

"A weak moment!" he gibed.

Cathleen decided that his grin was insufferably tolerant and male. "Yes. You took advantage of me."

"Oh, come on, Cath, don't try that third-rate virgin act on me."

"I'm not trying any sort of act. I was emotionally upset, and it was wrong of you to start, knowing the state I was in."

"Apparently it was the proper state in which to reach you. We came closer to blending, to truly being one, than ever before. Didn't it tell you anything? We belong together, no matter how hard you fight it!"

"I admit I want you. It'd be silly to deny it. I'll even admit I love you."

"Thank you very much," he inserted sarcastically.

"But it doesn't mean we should get married. You're poison for me, Casey."

"We've been through this before," he interrupted roughly, striding forward to grasp her arms. "What your argument boils down to is that you're scared to death of giving yourself to love. You're afraid there won't be anything left of you afterwards. I'm not your daddy, Cathleen, and that won't happen."

"Don't start in about that again."

"Listen to me, girl. You have two choices. You can stay here with Dusty, taking care of him as you always have, figuring the evil you know is better than the one you don't. You can chase after him and sympathize and watch him like a hawk, wasting your youth and beauty and talent, ending up with nothing." She shivered in his grasp, closing her eyes as if to block him out. He shook her lightly. "At the same time you'll be ensuring Dusty's defeat. As long as he has you to cling to and take care of him, he doesn't have to stand up and be a man. He doesn't have to shake his alcoholism. You'll always be there to pull him out. Don't you see? By helping him, you encourage his habit. You make him dependent on you."

Cathleen's eyes flew open. "No! How dare you?"

"You do it with all the love and good will in the world, but if you're his backbone, he doesn't need to develop one himself. You can stay with him in your symbiotic life. That's one choice. Or you can leave and let Dusty choose his own way. Let him fall on his face or rise, whichever, but at least it'll be his own decision. You can come to me. Live with me, marry me, whichever you want, but make a commitment, take a chance. Let me give you enough love to make up for the dry years and enough freedom to become whatever you want."

Cathleen stared at him, her eyes widening at his impassioned plea. When he stopped, she couldn't move or speak. Casey leaned down and kissed her lightly on the forehead. "I love you, Cathy. I hope you opt for life."

Casey strolled away, leaving Cathleen gaping at his back. He continued out the den and through the kitchen without a backward glance. Cathleen heard the kitchen door close softly. Moments later the engine of his car started. Cathleen sank onto the nearest chair, dropping her head into her hands. She was depleted, weary, drained of love and passion. She also floated in the hazy warmth of satisfied love. Anything seemed possible, even likely. How could she doubt the power of love when she had responded the way she had to Casey? Yet how could she hope for anything, trust in anyone, when the world had come crashing down around her again?

Cathleen groaned, shaking her head, and rose. Things would seem clearer in the morning. A good night's sleep worked wonders with problems. If she went to bed now, she wouldn't have to face Lynette with the news of Dusty's fall from grace. Cathleen stumbled into her room and disrobed, tossing her garments haphazardly over the nearest chair. She didn't bother to find a nightgown, simply crawled between the sheets clad in her underwear. As soon as her head hit the pillow, she was asleep. Dimly she heard the sound of a car in the driveway later and then Lynette tiptoed into the room. Cathleen slid back into sleep.

She awoke the next morning much less tired, but still racked by doubt and confusion. Lynette was asleep in the other bed. Cathleen slipped out of the room quietly. She showered and dressed, then occupied her hands by fixing a big breakfast. Cooking gave her an excuse not to think. Lynette soon entered the kitchen, clad in a girlish nightgown of pink cotton. She yawned widely. "Mmmm. What are you cooking?"

"Bacon, eggs and pancakes."

"Good Lord, are you fattening us up for the kill?"

Cathleen giggled. "Not you. Though I imagine Dusty's probably expecting his execution. In fact, the way he's feeling about now, I imagine he'd welcome it."

Lynette's head snapped toward her. "What do you mean?"

"He has a monumental hangover, I'm sure."

"Oh, God." Lynette sighed and sank into one of the kitchen chairs. "That man. He fell off the wagon?"

"With a vengeance. Casey and I found him under a pool table at a bar, one drink short of oblivion."

"You and Casey?" Lynette was diverted. "Are you two back together?"

"No," Cathleen replied hastily, regretting her words. "I just called him. I—I tried to call Jack, but you were gone."

"Yeah, we spent the day on the lake. What are you going to do about Dusty?"

Silently Cathleen wondered why Lynette always assumed that it was "you" and not "we" who would have to deal with Dusty's behavior. She wondered when and where it was that she had taken on the role of problem solver. It had occurred too far back to remember. Cathleen flipped a pancake and rubbed the frown from her forehead with her other hand. "I don't know. I haven't talked to him yet. He's still passed out. My first thought was to call the Villa and talk to his counselor. Maybe I can take Dusty out to see him today."

"Sounds good to me."

Cathleen expertly tossed a pancake onto a plate and slapped a pat of butter on top. She set the pancake platter on the table, added the plate of bacon and turned back to the stove to scramble eggs. She sprinkled various herbs on them, following Casey's recipe. As she'd already found in so many small ways, the reminder of him was razor sharp. Lynette dug into the breakfast with relish, but Cathleen discovered she wasn't hungry.

Instead of eating, she crossed over to the telephone and dialed the familiar number of the Oakcrest Villa. It took several minutes to get through to Dusty's counselor. He finally came on the phone, breathless, as if he'd run. Cathleen explained Dusty's lapse of the evening before. The news didn't elicit even a sigh of disappointment. "Has he been attending the group sessions?"

"Yes, except when we were on tour."

"Okay. Bring him out here if you can. How is he this morning?"

"Asleep," Cathleen answered succinctly. "If I know Dusty, he'll be so penitent when he wakes up that he'll be eager to come."

"Let me see, I have an open appointment at two-thirty. Is that all right?"

"We'll be there."

"All taken care of?" Lynette asked cheerfully as Cathleen returned to the table.

"Yeah." Cathleen glanced down at her plate. The eggs were cold and looked even less appetizing than they had before. She shoved her plate to one side and poured another cup of coffee.

There was a soft scraping sound in the hall. Cathleen turned in that direction. Dusty appeared in the doorway, moving carefully, his face lined with pain.

"Hello, Dusty," Cathleen greeted him, the conflict of emotions within her making her voice stiff. She was always uncertain what to say or do the morning after one of Dusty's binges. Anger and bitterness flowed in her, but because she didn't want to be punitive, she tried to suppress them.

"Hi, honey." Dusty raised his head, but didn't quite meet her eyes. His awkward demeanor matched hers. "Good morning, Lyn."

"Good morning."

He made his way to the table and sat down. "I could use a cup of coffee."

Lynette poured him a cup. Cathleen asked, "Breakfast?"

He shook his head faintly. "Not yet." His eyes slid toward the bowl of eggs and quickly away.

Cathleen picked up the food from the table and set it on the counter, out of his sight. Dusty raised the coffee mug to his lips. Cathleen noted that his hands trembled slightly. Lynette glanced from her father to her sister and took a final swig of coffee. "I think I'll take a bath and get dressed," she announced and disappeared from the room.

Cathleen went straight to the heart of the matter. "I've made you an appointment with Frank Muller at the Villa this afternoon."

Dusty nodded and rubbed his hands across his face, still avoiding looking at her. "Okay." Cathleen moved away to scrape the food on her plate into the sink. Dusty started speaking again, as she had known he would, and her muscles tightened all over. "Honey, I'm sorry about last night. I don't know what happened. I figured I'd have one beer. It was hot, and I kept thinking how good it would taste. I decided one beer wouldn't hurt." He shrugged. "It got away from me."

"It always does," Cathleen snapped before she could stop herself. She wished she didn't feel so cold and empty inside, or at least that she could hide the feelings from her father. It didn't do any good to get angry. She'd found out long ago how useless her disapproval or anger were in the face of his habit.

"Hell, I'm no good to you or anyone else." Cathleen knew that he was beginning his litany of despair and self-hatred, as if despising himself for what he'd done would somehow erase it. She hated talks like this as much as she hated his drunken sprees. Cathleen watched him as he spoke. His gaze flickered here and there, but he never looked straight at her. His attitude was that of a cowed man; he used the furtive, apologetic gestures and speech of a prisoner to his jailer or a child to his keeper. His fingers twisted nervously together as he spoke.

"Oh, stop it, Dusty!" Cathleen cried out. "I don't want to hear it. You don't have to say it to me."

"I disappointed you. I know how much you'd hoped I would stay on the straight and narrow. And I will! From now on, I'm not taking a drop. I found out yesterday I couldn't drink even a little without getting into deep trouble. Now that I know, I can't wonder about it and delude myself into thinking it would be all right. Really, it was a good thing. Now I know my limits. I know what I can do and what I can't."

She had heard very similar arguments many times before, but she refrained from pointing that out. It helped Dusty to believe his evasions and lies. He cherished his false hopes. Maybe that was why she was set against hoping. The thought stopped her. It was obvious now that she saw it. Her parents had been unstable. She hungered after stability. Her father was a liar at worst—at best one who saw the world through rose-tinted glasses. She clung to reality so fiercely that it became pessimism. In her scramble to escape her parents' fates, she had built a small, circumscribed world, the opposite of what she had known as a child.

In her world, everything was straight and true, clearly recognizable and easily followed. It was also insular and often pigeonholed. She had cut out the things that might make her like her parents—music; wild, passionate love; zest for the future. What would she have when all was said and done, she wondered, except a life unlike her parents'? That wasn't the same as having a life of her own. Her life was as shaped and ruled by her parents as if she had followed faithfully in their tracks.

Deep inside, Cathleen began to tremble. Was Casey right? Had she clung to her father and shut out her mother simply to make things fit her boxy world? Had she made her mother a scapegoat, just as she had made one out of Casey? Was her rejection of Casey cowardice? A last-ditch attempt to bring her world back into its proper order?

She remembered the way she had made love last night, wild and raging with passion, as if the suppressed parts of her were fighting to get out. It was scary, just as marrying Casey would be scary. She wasn't used to taking risks. She thought about what Jack had said the other day: "You have to take risks or you might as well give up and die. You *are* dead. They just haven't put you in the ground yet."

Slowly Cathleen stood up. She quivered with fear inside, although she kept her back straight as she faced her father. Dusty's voice trailed off and he looked up, puzzled. Cathleen spoke calmly but quickly, as if to get the words out before she lost the courage. "Daddy, I made you an appointment with your counselor at two-thirty. That's all I'm going to do. If you want to talk to him, it's up to you. I won't be driving you. I plan to see a couple of people this afternoon."

Dusty blinked, surprised. "All right. I can do it myself."

"I hope so. I hope you can do everything yourself. Because I won't do it for you. They told me this at the Villa a long time ago, but I guess I'm slow to absorb things. I understand now. I won't be your keeper anymore. I won't run around finding your bottles and pouring the liquor down the sink. I won't chase you down and sober you up or put you to bed. From now on, whether you drink or not is your responsibility. Just as it'll be your responsibility whether you stay with your career or go back down the tubes. I love you very much, but I have my own life to live. By staying here and taking care of you, I'm hurting us both. Do you understand what I'm saying?"

Dusty looked old and very tired. His answer was almost a whisper. "Yeah, I understand."

"Okay. I'm going to Casey's. I won't be home this afternoon. You and I have a date to sing tonight at the Grand Ole Opry. We're supposed to go onstage at nine twenty-five. I'll be there. I'll leave it up to you whether you show." She hesitated a moment, then swung away and strode down the hall to her room. She picked up her stage makeup case, the plastic-wrapped costume for that night and her handbag. Then she hurried out of the house. Dusty still sat where she had left him, studying the grain of the table.

First Cathleen took a side trip to Brentwood, a wealthy

community where many country and western stars lived. The houses were huge, expensive and set far back from the road. Cathleen drove through the area slowly. It had changed in the last ten years.

But the turn-in to Greenwood was the same, as was the curving asphalt drive leading to the columned plantation-style house. Greenwood stood on a slight rise, a monument to conspicuous consumption. Yet there was a certain beauty to its grandeur despite its ostentation, and to Cathleen it had the sentimental loveliness of childhood memories. Her eyes misted slightly and she blinked away the moisture. She parked directly in front of the mansion and strode to the front door.

Here was another innovation: a video camera positioned above the door to inspect visitors. An intercom came on, and a male voice asked her to identify herself. Cathleen spoke up clearly, "I'm Cathleen Richards, Stella's daughter."

Moments later a rather tough-looking individual opened the door. His eyes swept down her suspiciously, but he stood aside to let her enter. One of Stella's watchdogs, Cathleen surmised. "She's in her office. You know where it is?"

"Yes, of course."

Cathleen set off down the hall and turned to the right. The office was at the end of the second hall. Its door stood wide open, and she could hear Stella's distinctive voice. She was talking about rates and tax-exempt bonds. Cathleen presumed that she was talking to her financial advisor. Cathleen paused uncertainly at the door. Stella was leaning back in her high leather chair, eyes closed, the telephone receiver cradled on one shoulder. She opened her eyes and searched through the things on her desk, then glanced up and saw Cathleen standing in the doorway. Her expression stiffened into a mask. For an instant there was nothing but silence in the room. Then she said into the phone, "Larry? I'll call you back. Something important just came up. Bye."

She replaced the receiver and stood in one graceful movement. Cathleen saw that Stella looked as lovely and stylish as ever in camel-colored slacks and a pastel-striped blouse. Her private attire was far less flamboyant than her public costumes. "Cathleen! Has something happened? Is Lynette all right? Dusty?"

"Hello, Mother. Lynette's fine. She's marrying Jack Beaudry. Has she told you yet?"

"Yes, a couple of weeks ago. I don't understand—" She broke off and came toward Cathleen. "Why don't we go to my sitting room? It's more comfortable."

They went up the stairs to the cozy sitting room adjoining the master bedroom. Stella had redesigned it since Cathleen had last seen it. She sank into a soft, flowered sofa. "I didn't come about anybody else," she began, her voice tremulous with nerves. "I came about me." Stella sat across from her, head slightly tilted, waiting. "I . . . uh . . . I wanted to apologize for my behavior at Dusty's banquet. In fact, for the past several years."

Stella's eyes widened and she made a gesture to rise, quickly aborted. "It's all right. I made more than my share of mistakes, too. I never treated you like I should have. It wasn't that I didn't love you, you know, but you and Dusty seemed so close that I felt left out. And I . . . resented it. I'd like a second chance." Stella's voice lilted endearingly, her eyes forming a question.

"Me, too," Cathleen answered.

They talked for close to an hour. Cathleen knew that the relationship between her mother and herself would never be the friendly, easy one of some mothers and daughters. They were too dissimilar in some ways, too alike in others. Too many things had happened between them. But at least, Cathleen thought as she left the huge house, at least it was a beginning, a possibility. She had taken the chance.

Casey slid the cassette tape into the slot and adjusted the volume. A simple piano and guitar intro flowed out into the room, then Cathleen's voice started, pure and unbelievably beautiful. Casey shut his eyes against the bittersweet flood of feeling and leaned back in the modernistic leather chair. He wondered why he tortured himself by listening to her voice, yet he knew he wouldn't cut it off for the world.

The weeks since Cathleen had walked out of his life had been difficult—worse than difficult. They had drained him, cut him, twisted him with pain. There had been days when he thought he couldn't make it without seeing her. He would start for the telephone, intending to beg her to come back. Only the knowledge that if he gave in now he would never know the full joy of her love kept Casey from asking her back on any terms.

Last night, when they made love, he had been shaken by the experience as much as Cathleen had. He had never experienced such rapturous melding, even with her. He had been certain that Cathleen had given herself to him completely. When she had stunned him by again refusing to marry him, he had lashed out at her. He had been coldly furious when he left her house, and spent most of the night pacing, cursing and smoking, a habit he'd given up years ago.

He'd run out of cigarettes and the anger had drained away, leaving a cold sickness in its place. Casey wanted Cathleen so badly that he didn't think he could last another day. If he accepted her desire to be only lovers, she would be his again. He wouldn't have what he wanted, but at least he'd have some part of Cathleen, however incomplete.

Her recorded voice swirled around him, drowning out the sounds of a car door slamming outside and a key rasping in the lock. He didn't hear Cathleen until she was in the room. Her heels clicked on the hardwood floor, and he turned, puzzled. For a moment he thought she was unreal, a figment dredged up from his wishful thinking. Casey stared without moving.

She paused hesitantly, her expressive blue eyes darkening with concern. "Casey?"

"Cathleen!" He bolted out of his chair and strode toward her. He pulled her to him, encircling her with his arms and resting his cheek on her head. His muscles were tight and demanding against her. "Cathy, ah, Cathy." He kissed her hair and neck, tilting her face up to receive his rain of kisses.

"Wait, Casey, wait," she protested, pulling away as far as she could. He stiffened. "Let me get out what I came here to say. I want to marry you." At his silence she stumbled on uncertainly, "That is, I mean, if you still want me."

"Still want you!" he echoed disbelievingly. "Will tomorrow be too soon for the ceremony?"

She laughed, and he kissed her, stifling the sound. For a long moment they clung together, as if they had forgotten the full wonder of being in each other's arms and were memorizing it again. They sank to the floor, kissing and caressing each other, not making love, but simply reassuring themselves of each other's existence. Cathleen kissed Casey's fingertips one by one. "I have one condition."

"I accept it."

"Don't you want to hear it before you agree?"

"After the past three weeks, I'd agree to anything, so it doesn't matter."

Cathleen chuckled. "I'll tell you anyway. I know you want me to become a singer. I'm perfectly happy to record. I'll even go on tour with you, if you want, but I won't tour by myself."

Casey laughed delightedly. "Hell, honey, I don't want you to go on tours. I want you to stay with me. That's an easy condition."

"I guess I'm just easy." She smiled up at him. His eyes glinted as he bent to kiss her fiercely.

They made slow, sweet love on the floor of his studio, then lay together in delicious nakedness, making plans for their future. There was no thought of anyone or anything else that afternoon. They knew nothing but each other. It was with great reluctance that Cathleen finally drew away. "I have to shower and go."

"Where? Why?" He frowned.

"The Grand Ole Opry. Dusty and I are supposed to sing tonight, though I may be singing all by myself." She related the events of the day to him.

When she was through, he took her hand and kissed it in a serious, courtly gesture. "I'm proud of you, Cath. You have more character than a dozen people." She flushed beneath his gaze. Casey rose and reached down to pull her up, too. "Come on, let's shower. I'll go with you."

"You don't need to."

"I want to. Do you honestly think I'd let you out of my sight?"

They showered slowly, distracted by kisses and soapy touches that extended far past washing, and had to dress hurriedly and speed into Nashville. They entered the Grand Ole Opry from the back, and were greeted by the guard who barred the fans, then trotted down the hall to the dressing rooms. Casey waited in the hall while Cathleen dressed in the black satin suit and put on her makeup. The music from the stage kept time with her racing pulse. When she was done, she opened the door to show off her flattering costume to Casey.

He lounged against the far wall, and beside him stood Dusty, dressed in his black and silver suit. Cathleen stopped. Her heart began to thud. She hadn't admitted until now how afraid she had been that Dusty wouldn't show up. "Daddy," she breathed, a trembling smile touching her lips.

"Hello, sweetheart." He hugged her and she was joyously aware that he smelled only of cologne—no alcohol. "Did you think your old man would desert you?"

"I'm glad you didn't."

"Since you're getting married, I'll have to take care of myself. 'Bout time, don't you think?"

She nodded, swallowing tears, and took the hand he

offered. She smiled at Casey, and he clutched his heart, making a face as if he'd been mortally wounded by her smile. "I have to go onstage now," she said mundanely, her eyes telling him that she loved him.

He answered her in kind. "I'll be waiting for you, darlin'."

Silhouette Sensation

COMING NEXT MONTH

TOO GOOD TO FORGET
Marilyn Tracy

A stranger stumbled into Katherine's life one night, bloody and confused. He thought he was her husband—Sam McDonald ex-CIA agent turned novelist. It was impossible. *There was no Sam McDonald*; he was a figment of her imagination... So who was this man?

'Sam' was a treasury agent suffering traumatic amnesia. His loving caresses lured Katherine into living a dangerous fantasy. When he regained his memory, would he forget her?

LIAR'S MOON
Mary Anne Wilson

Michael Conti saw Alexandria Thomas committing a near-perfect crime. Only his intervention kept her from walking away with the booty. He knew he should walk away from her there and then before he was dragged into something he wasn't ready to handle.

Alexandria knew she hadn't convinced Michael of her innocence, but she couldn't prevent herself falling in love with this tall, dark stranger. What was his interest in her? Why did he keep turning up at critical moments?

Silhouette Sensation

COMING NEXT MONTH

WORTH ANY RISK
Kathleen Korbel

When Abbie Fitzgerald found herself taken hostage and staring down the barrel of a gun, she decided that she would have an affair with the next man who walked through the door—*if* she lived that long.

Michael Viviano, the police officer who saved her life, was delighted with the idea and wanted to follow up on it just as soon as they caught the killer who was stalking Abbie...

SNOWFIRE
Heather Graham Pozzessere

Justin Magnasun hated reporters with a passion for good reasons. So when snoopy reporter Kristin Kennedy showed up at his isolated country house in the middle of a blizzard, *claiming* to be stranded, Justin was not very welcoming.

Kristin had stumbled across Justin by accident, but now she was interested and couldn't resist trying to piece together the puzzle of his past. She didn't think he was a murderer but, if he wasn't, *who* was?

TAKE 4 NEW SILHOUETTE SENSATIONS FREE!

Silhouette Sensations are thrilling romances for today's woman.

A specially selected range of romantic fiction seasoned with suspense. You'll also find glamour, sensuality and daring in each thoroughly modern tale!

So turn the page for details of how to apply and claim more free gifts!

YOU CAN ENJOY 4 SILHOUETTE SENSATIONS, A CUDDLY TEDDY AND A MYSTERY GIFT FREE!

Yes you can enjoy 4 Silhouette Sensations as your FREE gift from Reader Service, along with the opportunity to have 4 brand new titles delivered direct to your door every month!

You could look forward to receiving 4 Silhouette Sensations every month for just £1.85 each. Postage and packing is FREE! There's also our FREE Newsletter featuring authors, competitions, special offers and lots more...

It's so easy. Send no money now but simply complete the coupon below and return it today to:- **Silhouette Reader Service, FREEPOST, PO Box 236, Croydon, Surrey CR9 9EL.**

------------------------------------- ✂
NO STAMP REQUIRED

Please rush me 4 FREE Silhouette Sensations and 2 FREE gifts! Please also reserve me a Reader Service subscription. If I decide to subscribe, I can look forward to receiving 4 brand new Silhouette Sensations for only £7.40 every month. Postage and packing is FREE and so is my monthly Newsletter. If I choose not to subscribe, I shall write to you within 10 days and still keep the FREE books and gifts. I may cancel or suspend my subscription at any time simply by writing to you. I am over 18 years of age.

Ms/Mrs/Miss/Mr _____ EP69SS

Address _____

_____

_____ Postcode _____

Signature _____

Offer closes 31st November 1994. The right is reserved to refuse an application and to change the terms of this offer. One application per household. Offer not valid for current subscribers to this series. Valid in UK and Eire only. Readers overseas please write for details. Southern Africa write to IBS Private Bag X3010, Randburg 2125. You may be mailed with offers from other reputable companies as a result of this application. Please tick this box if you would prefer not to receive such offers. ☐

mps
MAILING PREFERENCE SERVICE